THE MEDICAL SCHOOL INTERVIEW

WINNING STRATEGIES FROM ADMISSIONS FACULTY

SAMIR P. DESAI MD
RAJANI KATTA MD

FROM THE AUTHORS OF SUCCESS IN MEDICAL SCHOOL

PUBLISHED BY

MD2B

HOUSTON, TEXAS

www.MD2B.net

The Medical School Interview: Winning Strategies from Admissions Faculty is published by MD2B, PO Box 300988, Houston, TX 77230-0988.

www.MD2B.net

Printed in the United States of America

9781937978013

Dedication

To all of the individuals who have taught us important lessons and helped us throughout our careers: our mentors, our teachers, our students, and our patients.

Acknowledgments

The authors would like to thank Brian Clinton, Biological Sciences Advisor at the University of Rhode Island, for his contributions.

ABOUT THE AUTHORS

Samir P. Desai, M.D.

Dr. Samir Desai serves on the faculty of the Baylor College of Medicine in the Department of Medicine where he is actively involved in medical student and resident education. He is a member of the Clerkship Directors in Internal Medicine, and the recipient of multiple teaching awards. He is an author and editor, having written fourteen books that together have sold over 150,000 copies worldwide.

His book *Success in Medical School: Insider Advice for the Preclinical Years* provides preclinical students with detailed knowledge and guidance to excel and position themselves for match success later in medical school. In 2009, he co-authored *The Successful Match: 200 Rules to Succeed in the Residency Match*, a well-regarded and highly acclaimed book that has helped thousands of residency applicants match successfully. He is also the co-author of *Success on the Wards: 250 Rules for Clerkship Success*. This book has helped thousands of medical students make the difficult transition from the preclinical to clinical years of medical school. *Success on the Wards* is a required or recommended resource at many U.S. medical schools, providing proven strategies for success in patient care, write-ups, rounds, and other vital areas.

As a faculty member, he serves on the medical school admissions and residency selection committees. His commitment to helping premedical and medical students reach their professional goals led him to develop the website TheSuccessfulMatch.com. The website's mission is to provide medical school and residency applicants with a better understanding of the selection process. Dr. Desai keeps applicants abreast of key information at The Successful Match blog. (www.TheSuccessfulMatch.blogspot.com).

After completing his residency training in Internal Medicine at Northwestern University in Chicago, Dr. Desai had the opportunity to serve as chief medical resident. He received his M.D. degree from Wayne State University School of Medicine in Detroit, Michigan, graduating first in his class.

Rajani Katta, M.D.

Dr. Rajani Katta is Professor in the Department of Dermatology at Baylor College of Medicine. She has authored over 50 scientific articles and chapters, and lectured extensively both nationally and locally on dermatology and contact dermatitis to students, residents, and physicians. She serves as the course director for dermatology in the basic science years, and has served as the clerkship director for the dermatology rotation. In these capacities, she has seen firsthand the importance of outstanding clinical evaluations in securing a position in a competitive specialty, and her insight in this area has helped students seeking these types of competitive positions.

Having advised many students over the years regarding the dermatology match process, she was determined to become expert in this area and share her knowledge, insight, and perspective. In 2009, she co-authored *The Successful Match: 200 Rules to Succeed in the Residency Match*. This book has quickly become the best-selling title in this field.

She is also the co-author of *Success on the Wards: 250 Rules for Clerkship Success*. This book has helped thousands of medical students make the difficult transition from the preclinical to clinical years of medical school. *Success on the Wards* is a required or recommended resource at many U.S. medical schools, providing proven strategies for success in patient care, write-ups, rounds, and other vital areas.

After graduating with honors from Baylor College of Medicine and completing her internship in Internal Medicine, she completed her dermatology residency at the Northwestern University School of Medicine.

CONTENTS

Chapter 1

Introduction

Why do you want to be a doctor? Why did you choose to apply to our medical school?

Many interviewers will ask variations of these basic, standard questions. And many applicants will have prepared answers for these. Many applicants, though, will get it wrong.

We've interviewed hundreds of applicants. Some we've grilled and some we've coached. And from these hundreds of applicants, we've learned one thing: almost every single one could have been better.

Write down your own answers to these questions, and then take a look at our approach.

Why our school?

You may be asked a number of variations of this same question:

- What qualities are you looking for in a school?
- Describe your ideal medical school.
- What interests you most about our school?
- Tell me what you know about our school.
- Why do you want to be a student here?
- What two or three things are important to you in a medical school?

While the question asks about the school, the best answers highlight the applicant. You need to make a strong case that YOU are the perfect fit for this exact school. Few applicants are able to do that well.

Here are examples of the typical responses that we've heard over the years:

"Well, I've lived here for three years so I know that I would want to live here. One of the things I like is the diversity and clinical opportunities you offer. I know I would see all kinds of different patient populations. The school has a good reputation which I know would help me get into a good residency program. The atmosphere is excellent, students help each other, and this is a place which will challenge me but not bring out the worst in me."

"I'm really looking for two things. First, a program that really integrates the clinical with the basic sciences. My impression is that [your school] does a good job with that. The second thing is the breadth of opportunities here. All the research that's going on. I can't imagine that it would be difficult to find many people I would be interested in working with."

"It seems like the school will help you reach your goals. You also have a lot of hospitals you can work at. Also, I'm interested in the International Health Track."

"I'll get a great education here. There are so many research opportunities. And students really seem to love the school. Also, the faculty is very involved with the students. Also having all the affiliated hospitals that you have here."

"The shorter basic science period really appeals to me. So does the way the basic science is structured, for example the way anatomy is spread over a number of semesters. I really like the medical center and Houston. The center is top notch."

What do all of these responses have in common? They're all underwhelming. While there a number of reasons for this, the main one is that all of these applicants end up sounding pretty generic. The responses are fine and nobody's sending up any red flags, but at the same time you'd be hard pressed to remember any of these applicants.

Why is that? First, most of these responses are too brief. Second, most of these responses lack specific details about the school, and all of them lack specific details about the applicant. Third, there's very little here that would convince the interviewer that this specific applicant would be a perfect fit with the school. And finally, there's nothing memorable in any of these responses. In other words, just about any applicant could have given the same response.

The biggest fail here is that every single applicant lost out on a valuable opportunity to impress the interviewer.

To see how a student could answer this question in a more compelling manner, let's meet Elena, an undergraduate student in Arkansas.

Elena's story

Elena grew up in a medically underserved area with a significant Latino population. There were relatively few primary care physicians in her community, and even fewer specialists. Several of Elena's relatives passed away of cancer, and Elena developed an early interest in oncology. After finishing medical school, Elena hopes to pursue residency training in internal medicine followed by fellowship training in oncology. She plans to return to her hometown to practice oncology, and would be one of only two oncologists serving a four-county area. In college, Elena worked with Dr. Garcia, a dermatology faculty member at a local medical school, to develop an instructional module to help primary care physicians differentiate benign from cancerous skin lesions. The main goal was to provide a resource for primary care physicians practicing in parts of the state lacking access to dermatologists. Elena was also involved in organizing and implementing skin cancer screenings in these underserved areas.

Elena's answer

"I first heard about your school from my faculty mentor, Dr. Garcia. Your school has an excellent reputation, and she spoke very highly of the education you offer. You're also well known for quality of teaching and diversity of patients, which I value. I also would love to live in Dallas, and have family in the Fort Worth area."

Analyzing Elena's answer

Be as specific as possible to confirm that your selection of their school was based on some thought and effort. Too often, applicants give a general answer. If you could give the exact same answer at another school, then your answer isn't good enough. If you examine Elena's response, you'll see that her answer, for the most part, was short on specifics. A better response is shown below.

Begin by researching the school thoroughly. What makes this school unique? What aspects of the school or its curriculum do you find particularly compelling? This information allows you to tailor your responses. In simple terms, if the school highly values research, and you have an interest or experience in that area, then you need to discuss it.

If a faculty member recommended the program, then by all means say so, as Elena did. Schools like to know that they're well regarded. Speaking with someone who has firsthand knowledge of the school also demonstrates that you've taken the time and initiative to learn as much as you can about the school. It demonstrates the seriousness of your interest.

There are also certain responses that you need to avoid at all costs. Avoid answers that confirm a disconnect between what you're seeking and what the school offers. Never put down another school. Lastly, while the geographic location of the school may be a major factor in your interest, avoid offering location as the only or initial reason for applying to the school.

A better answer

"I first learned about your school through my faculty mentor. Dr. Garcia is a graduate of your school and she's always spoken highly of the training she received. I would love to be a medical student at your school for a number of reasons. In shadowing physicians, I've learned that it's important to go to a school that places an emphasis on clinical skills. Your school has a reputation for being a leader in clinical skills development. The early patient contact, frequent observation of skills followed by regular feedback, and simulation lab are particularly appealing to me. It's also important to me that I develop a strong foundation for the practice of high quality care with patient safety in mind. That's why I'm really excited about your unique patient safety curriculum. And finally, I know that your school has a track for the underserved, and I could really see myself thriving in this track. In college, some of my most rewarding experiences occurred when I was involved in organizing and implementing health fairs for rural communities. Receiving education in caring for an underserved population would be fantastic because I would like to make this an important part of my future career in medicine. I grew up in a medically underserved area, and would like to return to my hometown as an internist and oncologist. On a personal note, I do have family in the Forth Worth area, and training in Dallas would allow me to spend time with family."

In the following pages, you'll learn how to create this type of response.

A response that is very memorable. A response that confirms that you have the qualities that this medical school seeks. The type of response that confirms to the interviewer that you are the perfect fit for their medical school. The type of response that so impresses the interviewer that they become your advocate in committee meetings.

In the next 200+ pages, we'll review, in depth, the medical school interview. You'll learn how critical the interview is in the admissions process. The Association of American Medical Colleges (AAMC) evaluated the importance of 12 variables on admissions decisions. Of these, the MCAT score was rated sixth. Cumulative science and math GPA was rated third.

The most important factor in admissions decisions was, in fact, the interview.

You'll learn why the interview is so important to admissions officers. It's widely recognized that the best physicians have more than just great scores and grades. The most effective physicians display a number of non-academic attributes. These traits are difficult to evaluate, and admissions officers rely on the interview to help assess these traits. In Chapter 3 we present the results of a survey of admissions officers that focuses on traits that are valued in future physicians. Over 20 traits are ranked, including such items as motivation for a medical career, empathy, personal maturity, service orientation, and leadership.

Research has also identified qualities that may hurt your chances for admission. Some of these qualities can be surprisingly easy to display in the high-pressure setting of an interview. It's easy to predict that schools don't seek out blunt or uninhibited applicants, but even traits such as self-critical or apologizing can hurt your chances.

You'll learn how to research the medical school, and how to determine the type of student that the school seeks. With an analysis of your own strengths and skills, you can begin to tailor your responses. Chapter 9 reviews the typical interview questions, and provides examples of other students' thoughtful, tailored, and memorable responses.

In the past, students could focus just on these types of standard interview questions. Why do you want to be a doctor? Why are you interested in our school? What are your strengths? While some schools still utilize the standard format of one interviewer speaking to one applicant for 30 minutes, many schools are adopting other formats.

Are you prepared for the MMI? This format has been utilized by such diverse medical schools as Stanford, Oregon Health Sciences University, Virginia Tech, UC Davis, and University of Cincinnati, among others. In the multiple mini-interview, the applicant moves from one station to another over a two-hour period. At each station, he or she is asked to respond to a question, a short structured scenario, or even a task. In Chapter 5, you'll learn more about the MMI, as well as the behavioral interview, the panel interview, and the group interview, among others.

In the following chapters, we review, in detail, other important aspects of the interview. You'll learn how to maximize your interview preparation, and what to expect on the typical interview day. We review the common pitfalls that we've seen multiple applicants make, over and over again, every interview season. You'll even learn about the best thank you notes, how to handle an offer of acceptance, and what to do if you're on the waitlist.

The recommendations in this book are based on multiple sources. Throughout the book, you'll see quotes from many different admissions officers. There's also been a substantial body of research on the topic of predicting which applicants will make the best physicians. We've included the results of these research studies, which have shaped and guided our recommendations. Lastly, the recommendations are based on extensive discussions with admissions faculty as well as applicants. Dr. Desai has served on the admissions committee at Baylor College of Medicine for over 10 years. He also provides interview preparation services for applicants to other medical schools, and both he and Dr. Katta have advised many applicants as they prepare for the residency match. The Successful Match is the best-selling title in the field of residency match preparation. In this book, we've applied the same combination of evidence-based advice and insider knowledge.

From personal experience, we've seen what works in an interview, and we've seen where students have failed. In the next 200+

pages, you'll learn how to apply these lessons to your own application. It's taken years of intense work for you to reach this point, and receiving an invitation to interview is a strong vote of confidence from the medical school. In the following pages, you'll learn how to make the most of this opportunity in order to reach your goal: medical school.

Chapter 2

The Interview and its Importance in the Admissions Process

Rule # 1   **The interview is a critical factor in the medical school admissions process.**

When applying to medical school, the admissions interview is a critical factor. In fact, at some schools it's <u>the most important</u> factor. In one survey of medical schools, over 60% of surveyed schools reported that the admissions interview was the most important factor in the selection process. [1]

A more recent survey provides further data. In 2011, the Association of American Medical Colleges (AAMC) published a survey that evaluated the importance of 12 variables on admissions decisions. These variables included total MCAT scores, science and math GPA, and the interview. Many students are surprised by the results.

Of the 12 variables, total MCAT score was rated sixth in importance. Cumulative science and math GPA was rated third. [2]

The <u>most important factor</u> in admissions decisions was in fact the interview. The interview received a mean importance rating of 4.5 (scale of 1 [not important] to 5 [extremely important]).

Did you know...

Dunleavy and colleagues examined the undergraduate grade point averages and MCAT scores of all applicants accepted into medical school in 2008, 2009, and 2010. They found that high undergraduate GPAs and MCAT scores do not guarantee admission.

Among applicants with undergraduate GPAs and MCAT total scores of at least 3.8 and 39, respectively, approximately 8% failed to gain admission to any of the medical schools to which they applied.[2]

Why is the interview considered so important, especially in relation to factors such as MCAT scores and science GPAs? "Medical educators agree that success in medical school requires more than academic competence," wrote the authors. "It also requires integrity, altruism, self-management, interpersonal and teamwork skills, among other characteristics."[2] Medical school faculty have long known that while academic variables such as scores and grades may predict preclinical performance, they're not as helpful in predicting which students will become good physicians. Studies have shown that scores and grades don't have as much predictive power, with respect to clinical performance, as do other factors.[3]

What does predict clinical performance? In one study, interview ratings of nonacademic attributes correlated strongly with subjective evaluations of clinical performance in required clerkships.[4] These nonacademic attributes included interpersonal skills, maturity, and motivation/interest in medicine.

Given these findings, med schools can't rely solely on objective data such as scores and grades. Noncognitive skills have significant value in predicting clinical performance, and since schools are limited as to how they can assess such skills, the interview takes on greater importance.

Importance of the Admissions Interview Based on Review of Medical School Websites	
Medical School	**Website Comments**
Vanderbilt University	Interviews are an important part of the application process because it provides the admissions committee with the opportunity to evaluate an applicant's interpersonal skills and intangible qualities that cannot be evaluated through MCAT scores, GPA, or other parts of the application.[5]
University of Connecticut	An important part of the admissions committee's final selections, the interview provides an opportunity to meet the applicant and to gather additional personal and supplemental data for the committee to evaluate the applicant...Interviews provide the admissions committee with personal impressions and insights on the applicant by evaluating, and putting in perspective, all aspects of the applicant's background, experiences, coursework, motivations, and values.[6]
UCLA	The interview is an important and integral part of the selection process. It gives the Admissions Committee an opportunity to learn more about the candidate and their ability to be part of the entering class.[7]
Penn State University	The interview is an essential component of the selection process. It provides vital information about the applicant that is impossible to obtain by any other means. Faculty interviews with critical evaluations are the only method within the admissions process for the assessment of the important nonacademic attributes of applicants. The Selection Committee places great importance on these evaluations in making decisions on admission.[8]
LSU Shreveport	High grades and/or MCAT scores alone are never enough. For those interviewed, impressions from the personal interview are exceedingly important.[9]

Rule # 2   **The interview can sink your chances of acceptance.**

"One of the most frustrating experiences in this job is to watch a student with excellent credentials, who I strongly suspect will make an excellent physician, go down in flames in the interview…"[10]

Quinn Capers, M.D.
Associate Dean of Admissions
Ohio State University College of Medicine

The interview is never just a formality. It can absolutely make or break your chances of acceptance.

In one study, admissions committee members rated applicants before the interview, using available application information, on a scale of 1 to 5. Criteria included motivation for medicine, commitment to serve others, leadership abilities, familiarity with issues in medicine, communication and interpersonal skills, and overall impression. Following the interview, and using the same scales, the committee members again rated the applicants.[11]

Researchers found that committee members often changed their ratings, sometimes markedly. Mean values for the measured qualities were found to change by as much as .47 of a standard deviation. They also found that communication and interpersonal skills ratings contributed most to predicting overall impression.

Admissions Directors Speak...

"In my position as Associate Dean for Admissions in the College of Medicine at The Ohio State University, I have screened thousands of applications, presided over admissions committee meetings in which the disposition of, collectively, hundreds of student applicants have been decided, and personally interviewed many applicants to our College. One of the most frustrating experiences in this job is to watch a student with excellent credentials, who I strongly suspect will make an excellent physician, go down in flames in the interview...It is definitely an advantage to put some serious thought and preparation into the interview, since medical schools generally only extend interviews to students who appear to have the right stuff to succeed."[10]

Quinn Capers, M.D.
Associate Dean of Admissions
Ohio State University College of Medicine

"Based on my experience, academic records and MCAT's are usually not an issue during admissions committee meetings, because with few exceptions applicants invited to interview are deemed to have the academic foundation to succeed in medical school."[12]

David Trabilsy
Former Assistant Dean of Admissions
Johns Hopkins University School of Medicine

"I think people are finally realizing that MCATs and grade point averages don't predict who will be a good doctor....There are other things that are equally important that tell you about whether someone will be successful as a medical student. A great deal of it has to do with building a total picture of an applicant: looking at what their educational and personal experiences have been, whether they have had obstacles to overcome, whether they have had incredible advantages that they have used to do something with, whether they've had an investment in people, whether or not they took the time to see a part of life that is different from their own so that they would appreciate it and treat it with respect and dignity if they saw it again as medical students and physicians. All of those things are very important and they are just as important as how you study for a chemistry exam or how well you prepared for the MCAT."[13]

Brenda Armstrong, M.D.
Director of Admissions
Duke University School of Medicine

Rule # 3   **Interviewers can become advocates.**

Your goal in an interview isn't just to make it through. Your goal is to impress your interviewer to such a degree that they feel compelled to become your advocate.

      To some students, this may sound impossible. When they think of interviewers, they typically think "gatekeepers." However, interviewers often become strong advocates for a particular applicant, even if they've only met during the course of one single interviewer. We've seen it many times in admissions committee meetings. This can be a powerful boost to your chances, since a vocal advocate for your candidacy can absolutely make the difference. Your goal in an interview, then, is to provide the interviewer with compelling reasons to support your application.

References

[1]Puryear J, Lewis L. Description of the interview process in selecting students for admission to U.S. medical schools. *J Med Educ* 1981; 56 (11): 881-5.

[2]Dunleavy D, Sondheimer H, Bletzinger R, Castillo-Page L. Medical school admissions: more than grades and test scores. *AIB* 2011: 11 (6).

[3]Mitchell K. Traditional predictors of performance in medical school. Paper presented at the annual meeting of the American Educational Research Association, San Francisco, California, March 1989.

[4]Meredith K, Dunlap M, Baker H. Subjective and objective admissions factors as predictors of clinical clerkship performance. *J Med Educ* 1982; 57: 743-51.

[5]Vanderbilt University School of Medicine. Available at:
https://medschool.vanderbilt.edu/admissions/campus-interview. Accessed February 22, 2013.

[6]University of Connecticut School of Medicine. Available at:
http://medicine.uchc.edu/prospective/apply/index.html. Accessed February 22, 2013.

[7]UCLA David Geffen School of Medicine. Available at:
http://ww.medstudentucla.edu/offices/admiss/interv.cfm. Accessed February 22, 2013.

[8]Penn State University College of Medicine. Available at:
http://www2.med.psu.edu/mdadmissions/interview-process/. Accessed February 21, 2013.

[9]LSU – Shreveport School of Medicine. Available at:
http://www.lsuhscshreveport.edu/Admissions/ReApplicants.aspx#personal. Accessed February 22, 2013.

[10]Ohio State University College of Medicine. Available at:
http://medicine.osu.edu/students/admissions/Documents/InterviewingTips.pdf. Accessed February 22, 2013.

[11]Nowacek G, Bailey B, Sturgill B. Influence of the interview on the evaluation of applicants to medical school. *Acad Med* 1996; 71 (10): 1093-5.

[12]Reflections of a Former Admissions Dean. Available at:
web.jhu.edu/prepro/Forms/Trabilsy.Admissions.Dean.doc. Accessed February 22, 2013.

[13]An interview with Dr. Brenda Armstrong. Available at:
http://www.vault.com/wps/portal/usa/vcm/detail/Career-Advice/Education-Advice/Wouldnt-You-Like-to-Know--An-Interview-with-Brenda-Armstrong,-Director-of-Admissions,-Duke-Medical-School.?id=5584. Accessed February 22, 2013.

Chapter 3

The Factors that Matter to the Decision-Makers

Rule # 4   **Respond to the goals of the interviewer.**

Why do medical schools require interviews? The answer is simple: they need to learn about qualities and skills that are separate from the ability to take exams. If your GPA and your MCAT score told the whole story, medical schools wouldn't need interviews. However, it takes much more than just excellent grades to make an outstanding physician. Although interviewers have a limited amount of time to meet and speak with you, they'll be doing their best to learn about all of your attributes.

The main goal of an interviewer is to determine if you have the necessary nonacademic attributes to succeed in medical school and clinical practice. Many students think that medical schools are most concerned about GPAs and MCAT scores. These academic indicators are important, but they don't tell the whole story. An applicant with a 42 on the MCAT doesn't equate to an outstanding physician.

Many interview questions focus on interpersonal skills, motivation, communication skills, compassion, and drive. Interviewers also try to determine "fit" with the school. Depending on the particular medical school, questions may be focused on your commitment to primary care, your interest in the underserved, or your commitment to research.

When I sit down with an applicant, I know the basics. I know their scores and their grades, I know what college they attended, and I know what work experience they've had. However, the application doesn't tell me what motivates this student. Why do they want to be a doctor? Is it because of the money, the status, or the job security? I know this applicant made great grades, but how do they handle pressure? Are they likely to lash out at their nurse colleagues when things get tense in the operating room? What will they do when faced with a patient in the emergency room who starts spitting at them? Is this the type of student who's focused on grades, or on knowledge? When they're taking care of a patient with heart failure, are they studying for the exam? Or are they the kind of student who's reading beyond the exam, in order to provide the best possible care for this patient? Is this the kind of student who would stay late to go over diagnosis and recommendations again and again for a patient who was scared and confused?

These are the types of issues I think about, and the answers to these types of questions aren't found in grades, scores, or essays. The answers to these types of questions aren't even found fully in interviews, although it's the best tool we currently have.

Did you know...

"Although intellectual ability and record of academic achievement are important elements contributing to the mastery of a challenging medical education experience, the Admissions Committee understands that other qualities are necessary to foster the development of a competent, compassionate and responsible physician," writes the Texas A & M College of Medicine. "Ability to communicate and interact, learning skills and attitude toward education, social consciousness, maturity, integrity of character, tolerance, and motivation for a career in medicine are among the characteristics sought."[1]

Did you know...

Dr. Janine Edwards, former Associate Dean for Student Affairs at the Medical College of Wisconsin, described the four major purposes of the medical school admissions interview: information gathering, decision-making, verification, and recruitment. She considered information gathering the most important function of the interview, as it provides a means to gather information that schools would be unable to obtain by other methods. This includes further information on nonacademic criteria such as motivation, leadership, and altruism. Schools also use the interview to verify the information provided by applicants. "By linking the interview to the initial review of the application materials, the committee can double-check or verify the authenticity of what has been presented," wrote Edwards.[2]

Rule # 5   **Medical schools seek certain qualities in their applicants.**

A review of the literature provides insights into the attributes and skills that medical schools seek. This table lists personal qualities that are valued by medical schools.

Personal qualities to convey during an interview[3-8]	
Ability to work with a team	Motivation/interest in medicine
Ability to solve problems	Communication skills
Ability to manage stress	Conscientiousness
Altruism	Leadership ability
Commitment to serve others	Listening skills
Critical thinking	Respect for others
Enthusiasm	Responsibility
Energy	Poise
Flexibility	Positive attitude
Effective time management	Reliability
Problem-solving	Honesty
Confidence without arrogance	Dedication
Recognition of limits	Compassion
Willingness to admit error	Empathy
Perseverance	Curiosity
Initiative	Determination
Intelligence	Work ethic
Maturity	Interpersonal skills

Which of the above personal qualities are most commonly assessed? A recent survey of admissions officers, representing 90% of U.S. medical schools, provides some answers.[9]

Personal Characteristics Assessed During the Admissions Interview	
Personal characteristics	Percentage
Motivation for a medical career	98%
Compassion and empathy	96%
Personal maturity	92%
Oral communication	91%
Service orientation	89%
Professionalism	88%
Altruism	83%
Integrity	82%
Leadership	80%
Intellectual curiosity	76%
Teamwork	74%
Cultural competence	72%
Reliability and dependability	70%
Self-discipline	70%
Critical thinking	69%
Adaptability	67%
Verbal reasoning	66%
Work habits	66%
Persistence	65%
Resilience	65%
Logical reasoning	56%
Adapted from the AAMC. Available at: https://www.aamc.org/download/261110/data/aibvol11_no7.pdf	

Note specifically that the top three qualities on this list are motivation
For a medical career, compassion and empathy, and personal maturity.
Logical reasoning, on the other hand, is ranked 21st in this list of
characteristics. These research findings should be used to help you prepare
the best possible responses.

Interview preparation involves much more than just learning
about what questions an interviewer is likely to ask. The best interview
preparation involves a thorough self-assessment. What type of volunteer
experience do you have? What does this experience say about your
motivations, your interests, your work ethic, and your drive? What type of
work have you done? How did you get that job? What does this say about
your persistence, determination, and ability to work with a team? What are
your extracurricular interests? What have these taught you about
teamwork, self-discipline, and adaptability? What obstacles have you
overcome in your life and education?

A thorough self-assessment is critical if you want to convey these
important qualities, skills, and strengths.

In Chapter 9, we review in more depth the common interview
questions. However, it's not very helpful to just jump to a question and
start rehearsing your answers. The best answers highlight your individual
qualities and unique experiences, and help you stand out from your
competition. This requires a thorough, thoughtful self-assessment.

As a simple example, many students give the same answer when
asked about their strengths.

Question: "What are your strengths?"

Answer: "I'd have to say that I'm an extremely hard worker, and
                 that I'm an excellent team player." And then they stop.

The student who's thought long and hard about all of his experiences has a
much more impressive, memorable response.

Question: "What are you strengths?"

Answer   "I'd have to say my drive, persistence, and ability to
                 work with a team to accomplish my goals. When I was
                 president of the AAA pre-medical interest group, our
                 organization learned of the need for children's books in
                 the waiting areas of the community clinics. I worked
                 with several other campus organizations, and
                 spearheaded a book drive and fundraising event that
                 ultimately was able to stock five clinics."

Look again at the list of qualities valued by medical schools, and then look at this student's response. What does this response make you think about? It makes me think service orientation. Leadership. Teamwork. Persistence.

In the table above, it's clear that while med schools value traits such as logical reasoning, such traits aren't sought out the way motivation for a medical career would be. In planning your interview responses, you should be thinking about the traits that are valued by medical schools. Your responses should then be focused on the qualities that you've exhibited and that medical schools seek.

Rule # 6   Certain qualities may harm your chances for admission.

Research has also identified qualities that would make applicants less likely to be admitted.[10] It can be surprisingly easy to display these types of qualities in the high-pressure setting of an interview.

- "Why doesn't your medical school offer the chance to do away electives in the third year?" [Overtones of argumentative]

- "I'm sorry, I wasn't prepared for that question, and I know that wasn't the best answer." [Apologizing]

- "Although my GPA is decent, I really wish I had done better in my freshman year, because otherwise my overall science GPA would have been better." [Self-critical]

Your interview preparation needs to ensure that you don't act or speak in a way that suggests any of these qualities:

- Meek
- Self-critical
- Apologizing
- Hurried
- Impatient
- Excitable
- Uninhibited
- Blunt
- Argumentative
- Pushy
- Easily angered

Admissions Directors Speak...

"Interviewers provide the admissions committee with personal impressions and insights on the applicant by evaluating, and putting in perspective, all aspects of the applicant's background, experiences, coursework, motivations, and values."[11]

University of Connecticut School of Medicine

"HWCOM Interview goals:

- To learn more about the candidate
- To evaluate a candidate's motivation, energy, tolerance for stress, analytical abilities, communication skills, decisiveness, initiative, knowledge of the profession, intellectual ability, and personality
- To provide the opportunity for the applicant to elaborate further on their application and qualifications
- To determine if the applicant fits the mission of HWCOM"[12]

Herbert Wertheim College of Medicine at Florida International University

----

"The purpose of the interview is to help the admissions committee evaluate both the non-cognitive and cognitive qualities of the applicant. Non-cognitive qualities include, for example, motivation, maturity, integrity, sensitivity, interpersonal skills, warmth, intellectual curiosity, the ability to withstand stress, ability to overcome adversity, and basis for the decision for a medical career."[13]

University of South Carolina School of Medicine

"Basically, they are trying to assess all of those things that are almost impossible to put down on paper. Interpersonal skill level, maturity, depth of motivation, soundness of decision, experiences, and the like. In general, they are trying to find out what kind of person you are and how motivated you are to study medicine."[14]

Miller School of Medicine at the University of Miami

"The interview day affords us the opportunity to learn more about you than your application can tell us...We want to get to know you; we are interested in the depth of your intellectual curiosity, your values and your commitment to a career of service. Your interviewers will ask you a variety of questions that will help them determine your communication skills, compassion for others and your motivation for practicing medicine in a multicultural society."[15]

University of South Alabama College of Medicine

Rule # 7   **You will be asked about, and judged on, your motivation to pursue a career in medicine.**

There's a good chance that you'll be asked "Why do you want to be a doctor?", or some variation thereof. In a recent survey of admissions officers (representing most U.S. medical schools), 98% of schools assessed motivation for a medical career at the time of the interview.[9] Your answer to this straightforward, basic question will allow the interviewer to make judgments about your motivations.

Why do students want to become doctors? In one retrospective study, researchers determined factors that influenced doctors to enter the field.[16] The main factors included:

- Desire to always become a doctor
- Wanting to help or work with people
- Selecting a profession that would provide an interesting career
- Aptitude for science subjects
- Urging by family/friends

A more recent study determined the motivating factors of students through focus groups. Researchers categorized the comments into eight overall themes.

Reasons Why Students Pursue a Career in Medicine	
Theme	Representative Comment
Relationships	"I think for me what I really liked was the patient/doctor relationship and just being able to have that connection with someone and being able to help them in a unique way."
Humanitarian impact	"Because I really want to make an impact on people's lives. That is what interested me to leave behind things that are unimportant."
Fulfillment	"I was looking for something that may be, when I am like 60, 70, looking back I can feel good about you know, what I did one day."
Knowledge	"I wanted a career where there would be continuous learning. Like you are always learning, you are always keeping up with medicine as it is constantly challenging on your brain and your way of thinking."
Power and influence	"The responsibility is like, you know, pretty much, you have the whole situation is in your hands and you can either basically screw it or make somebody better."
Status	"For me, it has kind of been that I really admire how people view physicians and doctors."
Financial security	"I have never heard of an unemployed physician or doctor."
Early experiences	"A lot of my friend's parents were doctors and you know, they have started talking to me a lot about, you know, what I was planning on doing, and I started to be more influenced by them."

Gillies R, Warren P, Messias E, Salazar W, Wagner P, Huff T. Why a medical career and what makes a good doctor? Beliefs of incoming United States medical students. *Education for Health* 2009; 9 (online): 331.

"Most medical school admissions committees feel that the most important reason for practicing medicine is to serve mankind," writes Dr. Quinn Capers, Associate Dean for Admissions at the Ohio State University College of Medicine. "So, while it is OK to mention your love of science and technology, and the fact that you love challenges, and the fact you have never really wanted to do anything else, it is a mortal sin of omission to not state your desire to help your fellow man as the main reason that you want to be a doctor. We regularly reject students with perfect GPAs and near perfect MCAT scores if we are not convinced that they have a serving heart."[17]

In expressing your motivation for medicine, "avoid cliché expressions," writes Dr. Jayant Shenai, Professor of Pediatrics at Vanderbilt University School of Medicine.[18] Instead, applicants are encouraged to be specific and support their statements with examples from their own experience.

Take the time to think back about your own experiences. What have you learned from your own personal, volunteer, or work experiences? Did these change your outlook, your perspective, or your behavior? "Real life, deep experience shows that you are a complex individual (not superficial) and that you understand the depth of life — what it is to be a human being; that you can be sympathetic," writes Dr. Steven Hausrath, former member of the admissions committee at the University of Texas Medical Branch at Galveston.[19]

Admissions Officers Speak...

"The answer to this question must be revealed in some way during the interview. If the response during the interview is 'well, I don't really know,' OR 'I can't really put it into words,' the committee response will be very clear: 'NO!'"[20]

Sylvia Robertson
Assistant Dean for Admissions
Pritzker School of Medicine at the University of Chicago

"We're always looking for people who see medicine as a calling. The thing I fear most is bringing people in who, in five or eight years, will be angry with their patients and the demands that medicine has put on them. I want to be sure they really get it, that they know medicine is more like ER than Marcus Welby, that there will be the 2 a.m. calls, that your kids will be waiting for you on the edge of the soccer field as it grows dark because you were supposed to pick them up 45 minutes earlier and got detained by a patient. We want to feel reassured that we're choosing applicants who will enjoy medicine all their lives. How do you put that down on paper?"[21]

Joyce Wahr, M.D.
Assistant Dean for Admissions
University of Michigan Medical School

Important Advice for Answering
"Why Do You Want To Be A Doctor?"

- Note that there are other ways to ask this question. Be prepared for these variations:

    - Why have you chosen to pursue a career in medicine?
    - What is your motivation for going into this profession?
    - Why medicine?
    - Why do you think you would make a good physician?
    - How do you know medicine is the right career for you?

- The interviewer wants to know how much thought you've given to your decision to pursue a career in medicine. Do you really understand what you're embarking upon? Is your knowledge of the field based on actual first-hand experience?

- Reread your personal statement to remind yourself of your motivations. Reflect on your experiences volunteering, shadowing, or working in a health care setting. What did you learn?

- Most interviewees profess an interest in science and the desire to help people as their primary motivations. Unfortunately, some applicants merely use clichés such as "I've always loved science" or "I want to help people." Far more compelling are answers that provide concrete examples to back up assertions. Evidence is what ensures that your responses are believable and sincere.

- When a student states that their main motivation to enter medicine is the desire to help people, an interviewer is going to look for further evidence. That one simple statement won't be enough. They'll ask questions about involvement in volunteer work, community service, and extracurricular activities. The interviewer's goals are to determine the breadth and depth of these activities. More importantly, he wants to confirm that the applicant was involved because of a sincere interest in helping others, rather than a sincere interest in strengthening their application.

- Was a personal or family illness a motivating factor? If so, be able to describe it, and discuss how the transformative nature of the experience led you to explore the field of medicine more deeply.

- A popular interview approach is to ask applicants to discuss a patient that left a mark or made a significant impression. Be prepared for the most/least favorite patient experience question.

Admissions Officers Speak...

"Because of the demanding nature of both the training for and the practice of medicine, motivation is perhaps the most salient nonintellectual trait examined by most admission committees. As a result, one of the questions most frequently asked of medical school applicants is 'Why do you want to be a doctor?'...Interviewers are always surprised and disappointed when applicants cannot articulate substantive answers. The lack of clear, enthusiastic-even impassioned-responses tells some interviewers that applicants have not explored or tested their desires to be physicians."[22]

Dr. Carol Elam
Associate Dean for Admissions
University of Kentucky College of Medicine

"Know yourself so well that you can articulate clearly your motivation to become a physician. Be able to detail how your activities support your claim of wanting to be a doctor."[23]

Louisiana State University Shreveport School of Medicine

Rule # 8   **Medical schools value direct exposure to medicine.**

"Motivation must be <u>demonstrated</u> not just espoused. You may want to 'help people', but without sufficient direct exposure to medicine, how do you know you want to become a physician, rather than a teacher, or social worker or other health care provider? The admissions dean and committee will want to know what experiences you've had to confirm your interest in medicine."[24]

David Trabilsy
Former Assistant Dean of Admissions
Johns Hopkins University School of Medicine

It may not have mattered as much in earlier years, but it's become very important in recent years. It's no longer enough to have amazing scores and grades, along with significant extracurricular accomplishments and volunteer activities thrown in. Some of your activities must involve direct exposure to the practice of medicine. Almost all applicants to medical school now have significant shadowing or direct medical volunteer experience, and some have actually worked in medicine. Your application needs to reflect your direct exposure to the practice of medicine, and your interview responses should include some mention of these.

Admissions Officers Speak...

"The Committee on Admissions uses the applicant's experience in the health care setting to determine if he or she understands the challenges and complexities of medical practice. The Committee is especially looking for direct contact with patients. Being a physician requires a strong commitment to patients that brings with it enormous self-sacrifice of personal energy and time with family and friends. Without direct patient care experience in the health care setting, many applicants fail to understand and appreciate these challenges and they are more likely to not finish their medical training or to become dissatisfied with their careers. In addition, clinical experience provides the applicant with an understanding of the challenges of dealing with patients who are often experiencing the most stressful time in their lives. The applicant is able to determine if he or she has the capacity to deal with patients in an empathetic manner under these difficult conditions. The interviewer almost always asks applicants to describe an encounter with a patient."[25]

University of New Mexico School of Medicine

Rule # 9   **Medical schools value demonstrated commitment to service.**

Assessing an applicant's desire and commitment to serve others is an important function of the admissions committee. "By considering applicants' humanitarian interests, medical school admission committees play a crucial role in helping medical schools fulfill their social contract with the public - the selection of competent and caring future physicians," writes Dr. Carol Elam, Associate Dean for Admissions at the University of Kentucky College of Medicine.[22]

Although the AMCAS and secondary applications provide some insight into an applicant's altruism, it is the interview that allows the school to delve deeper into the candidate's experiences and interests outside of the classroom.

- Has the applicant participated in community service?
- Have these experiences been meaningful to the applicant?
- What is the depth and breadth of this involvement?
- Do the applicant's experiences provide evidence of concern or compassion for others?
- Is the interest in service sincere or simply a means to secure a position in medical school?

While many applicants claim a deep and abiding commitment to service, their application materials just don't provide any support.

Where is the evidence provided by your experiences and activities? How have you demonstrated your commitment to service? The University of Michigan Medical School puts it this way: "Altruism, or the devotion to the needs of others, can be assessed through review of the applicant's activities such as participation in community service or volunteer activities, as well as responses to interview questions about the applicant's goals and desires for a life of providing patient care."[26]

Admissions Officers Speak...

"Has there been any effort to assist the people with whom the applicant lives, either at school or at home? What has the applicant accomplished that improved the society in which he or she lives? What has the applicant learned from this community involvement?"[27]

Dr. Jonathan Muraskas, Chairman of Medical School Admissions Committee
Loyola University Stritch School of Medicine

"People said they want the people taking care of them to be in the trenches as a partner. They wanted us to find those students capable of respect and dignity, those whose life experiences suggested significant maturity. We have to make sure these people who are coming to us to learn how to be doctors have the humanistic qualities to translate academic firepower into compassionate medicine."[28]

Dr. Brenda Armstrong, Associate Dean for Admissions at Duke University

----

"All successful applicants must have service/volunteer experiences. While most volunteer and service activities have value, commitment to serving others is most effectively demonstrated by uncompensated, on-going, hands-on, face-to-face engagement with individuals who are underserved, vulnerable, and have needs that can be addressed by the skill set of student volunteers."[29]

University of Alabama Birmingham School of Medicine

"The Committee on Admissions uses the applicant's record of volunteerism as an indicator of the applicant's commitment to the community and to society. A good physician recognizes the role that local, national and world communities play in the health of the individual as well as the health of public. The applicant's previous experience in the community provides perspectives on these important interrelationships."[25]

University of New Mexico School of Medicine

"Another area where motivation for a career in medicine is determined and evaluated is through the student's demonstrated commitment to service in the community. As a physician, one's entire life is devoted to serving others, requiring great sacrifice and a strong devotion to one's career."[30]

Florida State University College of Medicine

"There isn't one aspect that we put more emphasis on than another, but there is a strong feeling by the admissions committee at Yale that students exhibit some commitment to community service."[31]

M. Lynne Wootton, Director of Admissions at Yale University School of Medicine

Rule # 10   **Plan to reinforce, throughout your interview, your "fit" with this school.**

The concept of "fit" is a very important one for medical schools. "Is this applicant a good match for our school?"

"Each medical school has its own unique mission, curricular offerings, learning environment, and clinical programs," writes the Michigan State University College of Human Medicine. "Equally talented students may struggle in one environment, but thrive personally and academically in another."[32]

A quick review of med school websites reveals differing missions and goals. Some schools have a rich tradition of producing researchers. Others place more emphasis on primary care. Some schools have launched initiatives to graduate physicians who will care for patients in medically underserved regions of their states. There are military medical schools, historically black medical schools, and even schools with a religious bent.

Tip # 1

Carefully consider the school's mission as a part of your interview preparation. Be able to articulate why you would be a good fit for the school. Unfortunately, it's easy to go overboard when trying to demonstrate fit, and some applicants do. Interviewers value consistency and sincerity, and will evaluate whether your answers are congruent with the themes and evidence presented in your application.

Admissions Officers Speak...

"We also suggest that you visit the medical school(s) that interest you ahead of time to become familiar with the institution, its history and mission, its curriculum, and its place in the community or region where it resides. Admissions committee members are usually impressed with students who have done their homework, are knowledgeable about the medical school, and demonstrate enthusiasm about becoming a medical student at that institution."[33]

Edwin Taylor
Assistant Dean for Admissions and Records
East Tennessee State University James H. Quillen College of Medicine

Admissions Officers Speak...

"A major focus of our mission is to educate physicians interested in working with underserved populations (rural, inner city), particularly within Michigan."[34]

Michigan State University College of Human Medicine

"We want students who are attracted to life outside a major metropolitan area, who like wide open spaces."[35]

William Cathcart-Rake, M.D.
Campus Director
University of Kansas School of Medicine – Salinas Campus

"I look to make sure the applicants are a good match, that they're in sync with our mission. I look for well-rounded people and look for what makes them tick."[36]

Jacqueline Scolari, Ph.D.
Member of the Admissions Committee
Southern Illinois University School of Medicine

"Our applicants are above-average students who have a lot of volunteer experience. I want to see that they have some commitment to staying in central and southern Illinois."[36]

Penelope Tippy, M.D.
Member of the Admissions Committee
Southern Illinois University School of Medicine

"The committee is looking for evidence of intellectual ability, dedication to human concerns, communication skills, maturity, motivation, and potential for medical service in an underserved area of Ohio."[37]

Boonshoft School of Medicine at Wright State University

| Rule # 11 | Success in medical school requires a high level of personal maturity, and therefore schools seek evidence of this important trait. |

The training and study required to be a physician is physically and emotionally demanding. "The pressure cooker brings out all of the problems," writes Dr. John Delzell, Associate Chair of Medical Student Education at the University of Kansas, in his blog Education in Medicine. "It stresses them. It pushes them in ways that many of these students have never been pushed…I see students struggle because they have never been in this kind of situation. Students are young, they are often coming straight from undergraduate school. Students that come to medical school have often not had any real life experiences. They have not had a job, or had extensive life experiences."[38]

The interview is used to determine if you have the emotional maturity and stability to handle the rigors of medical school. Interviewers seek to answer these questions:

- Does this applicant have the ability to cope with stress? What evidence of that do I see in the application?
- What obstacles has she overcome? How did she overcome these?
- Has he reflected on his successes and failures? What has he learned about himself?
- Does she have the resilience to handle the challenges of medical school?
- Is she receptive to constructive criticism and feedback?
- Is he able to explain any weaknesses in his application in a mature manner?

While interviewers will seek answers to these questions in your application materials, they'll also ask you directly. An interviewer may ask "Tell me about a challenge you faced in college, and how you dealt with that challenge." It's important to reflect on your experiences so that you can answer this type of question with evidence of your emotional maturity, coping abilities, and coping strategies. Similar questions include:

- What did you find to be the most difficult aspect of college?
- Tell me about a challenging situation you encountered in college, and how you dealt with it.

- Tell me about a time you experienced conflict with a colleague, and how you handled it.
- What obstacles have you overcome on your path to medical school?
- College can be very stressful. How did you cope with the stress?
- I see that you had academic difficulty during your first semester. What did you do about that?

Admissions Officers Speak...

"Among these qualities the Committee pays close attention to maturity and evidence of effective coping strategies when challenging situations have occurred. Medical school by itself is demanding, and it is important to the Committee to know that you can balance other life events while maintaining focus on your education."[39]

University of Wisconsin School of Medicine and Public Health

Rule # 12   Integrity is the foundation of medicine.

The profession of medicine used to be held in the highest esteem. However, there have been numerous stories in the media of dishonest, unethical, and even criminal, physicians and medical researchers. From physicians who have committed Medicare fraud, to researchers who have fabricated research results, the media has had numerous stories to report.

This has tarnished our profession, and it's become even more important to medical schools to make sure that these types of individuals are not accepted. Interviewers aren't just looking for evidence of fraud. Understandably, they're turned off by insincerity or any hint of dishonesty. The Student Affairs Office at University of South Carolina states: "Interviewers universally indicate sincerity as one of the qualities they value most. Everything you say is worthless if the interviewer doesn't believe you are being honest. Experienced interviewers have great confidence in their ability to detect insincerity, and woe be the applicant perceived as insincere."[40]

Many students, prior to an interview, have no idea how easy and tempting it is to tell a little white lie. In fact, in one study, 34% of applicants actually admitted to not answering with the truth when asked a common interview question.

Did you know...

In one study, applicants were asked "What type of medicine do you wish to practice?" When asked this common interview question, 34% of applicants admitted to not answering truthfully.

Why would students lie? The offered reasons included:

"My desire goes against the goal of the college of medicine, such as trying to develop physicians who will practice medicine in rural areas."

"Heard from sources that revealing true desire could possibly hinder my interview."

"Interviewed by a MD outside of the aspect of medicine I am interested in."

"Was not sure how the interviewer would react."[41]

In a survey of admissions officers (representing 90% of U.S. medical schools), 82% of the schools assessed integrity at the time of the interview.[9]

Admissions Officers Speak...

"Applicants are expected to be forthright, open and honest in their responses to their interviewer's questions."[42]

Office of Admissions at University of Maryland

Do not "be dishonest (i.e., say you want to provide 'hot topic' care and it's not evident anywhere in your application)."[43]

Paula K. Davis
Assistant Vice Chancellor for Health Sciences Diversity
University of Pittsburgh

Rule # 13   **Prepare for questions related to professionalism.**

What is professionalism? The foundation of the medical profession rests upon the trust that patients place in their physicians. Professionalism focuses on this foundation of trust. Although it's been defined in many ways, the core values and elements agreed upon include honesty, integrity, compassion, empathy, the ability to communicate effectively with patients, and respect for others.

Although we think of physicians as highly compassionate and ethical individuals, lapses in ethics and professionalism can affect every level of our profession. These lapses can certainly occur in med school. The evidence indicates that unprofessional behavior in medical school is associated with subsequent disciplinary action of physicians by state medical boards.[44]

Ethically inappropriate medical student behaviors and attitudes[45]	
Arrogant	Insensitive
Brash	No give and take
Antisocial	Defensive
Rude	Indifferent
Condescending	Prejudiced
Power-seeking	Self-centered
Egocentric	Cocky
Amoral	Dishonest
Rigid attitudes	Selfish
Inflexible	Flippant
Isolated	Uncaring
Devious	Judgmental

Medical Student Speaks...

"Halfway through my medical school interview, I was asked to define professionalism. This was the first school, and only school, that asked me that question, and to be perfectly honest, I was caught a little off guard. At the time, I was still finishing my senior year at a large undergraduate university. Never before had I talked about or written a paper regarding the meaning of professionalism. Since this medical school was first on my list, I knew that I had to come up with something. Therefore, I just said what was in my heart. A professional needs to be honest, caring, possess integrity and humility. The actions of a professional at work need to be congruent with those actions displayed at home and in the community."[46]

Krych E, Vande Voort J. Medical students speak: a two-voice comment on learning professionalism in medicine. *Clin Anat* 2006; 19 (5): 415-8.

Admissions Officers Speak...

"It is the responsibility of the Admissions Committee to assure that our medical school selects those students with academic qualities that will allow for success in their medical studies, as well as attributes and experiences that will result in a skilled and empathic physician with a high degree of professionalism and strong communication skills."[47]

Chip Souba, M.D.
Geisel School of Medicine at Dartmouth University

"Members of the Admission Selection Committee value the attributes of professionalism, and help ensure that Nevada's students possess these exemplary qualities."[48]

University of Nevada School of Medicine

"Needless to say, the admissions committee is the group of people who stand between an interviewee and medical school. Thus, I decided to seek the advice of Beth Bailey, Director of Admissions at the University's School of Medicine. Bailey pointed to professionalism as one of the most important aspects of an interview. Specifically, she said interviewees should dress conservatively and should not wear excessive jewelry, cologne or perfume. She added that eating and drinking during an interview indicate a lack of professionalism. She also said that treating the interviewer with respect, not cutting him or her off, having good posture and maintaining eye contact are key. Although these may seem obvious, Bailey said applicants make these mistakes often and it costs them every time."[49]

Omid Fatemi, M.D.
(conversation with Beth Bailey, Director of Admissions at the University of Virginia School of Medicine)

Professionalism Questions Asked of Applicants at One Medical School[50]

- You come into the hospital one morning during your 3rd year internal medicine clerkship and smell alcohol on the breath of another medical student during hospital rounds on the ward. What issues would you consider important in coming to a decision about what to do?

- One of your established patients asks you to write her a prescription for an antibiotic. She is not having any symptoms but tells you it's for her brother who doesn't have any health insurance and can't afford the medication. What issues would you consider important in coming to a decision about what to do?

Rule # 14   **Prepare for questions that focus on medical ethics.**

What are your thoughts about the role of the pharmaceutical industry in medical practice? How would you handle a case of witnessed medical negligence by a colleague? Have you thought about the ethics of end-of-life care?

You need to.

You must be prepared to respond to ethical dilemmas during an interview. In an analysis of interviewee experiences, researchers found that approximately 10% of interview questions focused on resolving an ethical dilemma. The authors wrote that "admissions committees and faculty physicians deem it important to query prospective students about ethical issues."[51]

"Controversial and ethical topics have become somewhat standard among medical school interviews. They are worth researching in advance, and thus a word to the wise is: DO YOUR HOMEWORK."[52]

> Dr. Norma Wagoner
> Former Dean of Students
> University of Chicago Pritzker School of Medicine

Interviewers may present you with a difficult scenario, and ask how you would resolve it. You're more likely to respond well if you have a basic understanding of the issues surrounding the dilemma. You'll need to become well read on common controversies in medicine.

Since it's not possible to prepare for every possible scenario, we recommend that when you're faced with questions about a difficult and complex ethical situation you:

- Pause to gather your thoughts. What do you know of the situation based on your experiences and reading?
- Ask for clarification or further information, if needed.
- Share your knowledge of the topic with the interviewer.
- Discuss, out loud, the steps you would take to resolve the situation so the interviewer can assess your analytical and reasoning skills.
- Provide an answer or present options, and explain your rationale.

You won't simply be judged on the content of your answer. Questions about ethical scenarios are used to assess your poise under stress.

Interviewers also assess your ability to "think on your feet," and they'll evaluate your approach to a difficult situation.

You should avoid being "quick to judge, quick to respond without gathering data, or imposing your opinion on the patient when your opinions differ," writes Dr. Carol Teitz, Associate Dean for Admissions at the University of Washington School of Medicine. Dr. Teitz finds it acceptable to say, "I don't know," but this should be followed with "Here's how I would go about making a decision."[53]

Tip # 2

A useful resource to better inform you about ethical issues in medicine is the AMA Journal of Medical Ethics available at http://virtualmentor.ama-assn.org/.

Admissions Officers Speak...

"We try to find out how they will handle ethical concerns which will undoubtedly come up in medical school and beyond."[54]

James Hall, Ed.D.
Associate Dean for Student Affairs at the University of Illinois

----

"Some interviewers may ask you to present both sides of an issue and then select the one you believe in. Interviewers are not as much concerned about the applicants' belief systems, as they are about whether an understanding of the issue is present. For instance, it would not be good to state, 'I don't believe in fill-in-the-blank, and I would never treat or even refer a patient under these circumstances.' The interviewer is likely to see the applicant as being too rigid, rather than having the right to his or her belief system."[52]

Norma Wagoner, Ph.D.
Former Dean of Students at the University of Chicago

"Questions in this variety include queries about how you, as a physician, would respond if you encountered a drunk surgeon prior to his performing an operation. Another favorite is the question that asks what you would do if you witnessed a medical school classmate cheating on an examination. The golden rule in medical ethics is to always put the patient's best interests first. Thus, the 'correct' answer to any ethical dilemma posed is the one that places the patient's welfare above all else."[17]

Quinn Capers, M.D.
Associate Dean for Admissions at Ohio State University

Common Ethical Dilemmas Asked of
Medical School Applicants

- Doctor – patient relationship

    - Confidentiality
    - Informed consent
    - Patient rights
    - End-of-life decisions
    - Patient autonomy
    - Truth telling/disclosure

- Professionalism/professional misconduct

- Medical negligence/mistakes

- Relationship with the pharmaceutical industry

- Issues related to reproductive health

- Issues related to treatment of HIV/AIDS

- Genetics/stem cell

- Issues related to treatment of mentally ill patients

- Performing procedures/tests not medically indicated for reasons of defensive medicine

- Disagreements between patients/families and physicians about treatment decisions

- Treatment with placebo

- Transplantation/organ donation

- Research ethics

- Abortion

- Physician-assisted suicide

- Physician impairment (alcohol, drugs, or illness)

- Conflicts of interest

- Health care rationing

- Introducing medical students as doctors

- Practicing procedures on anesthetized or dead patients

References

[1]Texas A & M University College of Medicine. Available at: http://medicine.tamhsc.edu/admissions/faq.html#required. Accessed February 22, 2013.

[2]Edwards J, Johnson E, Molidor J. The interview in the admission process. *Acad Med* 1990; 65 (3): 167-77.

[3]Meredith K, Dunlap M, Baker H. Subjective and objective admissions factors as predictors of clinical clerkship performance. *J Med Educ* 1982; 57: 743-51.

[4]Murden R, Galloway G, Reid J, Colwill J. Academic and personal predictors of clinical success in medical school. *J Med Educ* 1978; 53: 711-9.

[5]Powis D, Neame R, Bristow T, Murphy L. The objective structured interview for medical student selection. *BMJ* 1988; 296: 765-8.

[6]Taylor T. The interview: one more life. *Acad Med* 1990; 65: 177-8.

[7]Collins J, White G, Petrie K, Willoughby E. A structured panel interview and group exercise in the selection of medical students. *Med Educ.* 1995; 29: 332-6.

[8]Shaw D, Martz D, Lancaster C, Sade R. Influence of medical school applicants' demographic and cognitive characteristics on interviewers' ratings of noncognitive traits. *Acad Med* 1995; 70: 532-6.

[9]Dunleavy D, Whittaker K. The evolving medical school admissions interview. *AIB* 2011: 11 (7).

[10]Jelley R, Parkes M, Rothstein M. Personality perceptions of medical school applicants. *Med Educ Online*; 2002: 7.

[11]University of Connecticut School of Medicine. Available at: http://medicine.uchc.edu/prospective/apply/index.html. Accessed February 22, 2013.

[12]Herbert Wertheim College of Medicine at Florida International University. Available at: http://medicine.fiu.edu/admissions/md/interview/index.html. Accessed February 22, 2013.

[13]University of South Carolina School of Medicine. Available at: http://www.greenvillemed.sc.edu/interview.shtml. Accessed February 22, 2013.

[14]Miller School of Medicine at the University of Miami. Available at: http://admissions.med.miami.edu/questions/interview-questions. Accessed February 22, 2013.

[15]University of South Alabama College of Medicine. Available at: http://www.usahealthsystem.com/body.cfm?id=1654. Accessed February 22, 2013.

[16]Allen I. Doctors and their careers. London: Policy Studies Institute; 1988.

[17]Ohio State University College of Medicine. Available at: http://medicine.osu.edu/students/admissions/Documents/InterviewingTips.pdf. Accessed February 22, 2013.

[18]Vanderbilt University School of Medicine. Available at: www.vanderbilt.edu/hpao/.../Medical%20School%20Interview.ppt. Accessed February 22, 2013.

[19]SUNY Plattsburgh. Available at: http://www.plattsburgh.edu/academics/prehealthadvising/insiderhausrath.php. Accessed February 26, 2013.

[20]University of Chicago Health Professions Handbook, the Office of the Dean of Students in the College, and the Newsletter of the Central Association of Advisors for the Health Professions. Available at: http://web.jhu.edu/prepro/health/Applicants/interviewing.html. Accessed February 22, 2013.

[21]University of Michigan Medical School. Available at: http://www.medicineatmichigan.org/magazine/2001/spring/pdf/v7admission.pdf. Accessed February 23, 2013.

[22]Elam C, Burke M, Wiggs J, Speck D. The medical school admission interview: perspectives on preparation. *NACADA* Journal 1998; 18 (2): 28-32.

[23]Louisiana State University Shreveport School of Medicine. Available at: http://www.lsuhscshreveport.edu/Admissions/FAQsInterviews.aspx. Accessed February 23, 2013.

[24]Reflections of a Former Admissions Dean. Available at: web.jhu.edu/prepro/Forms/Trabilsy.Admissions.Dean.doc. Accessed February 22, 2013.

[25]University of New Mexico School of Medicine. Available at: http://hsc.unm.edu/som/admissions/docs/Applicant%20Admissions%20Assessment.pdf. Accessed February 22, 2013.

[26]University of Michigan Medical School. Available at: http://med.umich.edu/medschool/admissions/apply/Admissions-Policies-Procedures.pdf. Accessed February 22, 2013.

[27]The Medical School Admissions Process: From MCATs to Interviews – What you need to know. Available at: www.iwu.edu/biology/images/Muraskas_talk.ppt. Accessed February 23, 2013.

[28]An interview with Dr. Brenda Armstrong. Available at: http://www.vault.com/wps/portal/usa/vcm/detail/Career-Advice/Education-Advice/Wouldnt-You-Like-to-Know--An-Interview-with-Brenda-Armstrong,-Director-of-Admissions,-Duke-Medical-School.?id=5584. Accessed February 22, 2013.

[29]University of Alabama Birmingham School of Medicine. Available at: https://www.uab.edu/medicine/home/education/prospective/min-require-consid/factors. Accessed February 23, 2013.

[30]Florida State University College of Medicine. Available at: http://med.fsu.edu/userfiles/file/PreMedHandbook.pdf. Accessed February 20, 2013.

[31]Franke M. Harvard pre-meds say summer job search not as stressful as believed. *Harvard Crimson*. Available at: http://www.thecrimson.com/article/1998/2/24/harvard-pre-meds-say-summer-job-search/. Accessed February 21, 2013.

[32]Michigan State University College of Human Medicine. Available at: http://mdadmissions.msu.edu/index.php. Accessed February 20, 2013.

[33]Taylor E, Elam C. The medical school application interview form the other side: suggestions from the medical school admissions office. *Advisor* 2009 (September).

[34]Michigan State University College of Human Medicine. Available at: http://mdadmissions.msu.edu/faq/pages/competitive_faq.php. Accessed February 23, 2013.

[35]Krupa C. Med schools seek right fit for rural practice. *American Medical* News. Available at: http://www.ama-assn.org/amednews/2011/08/08/prl20808.htm. Accessed February 23, 2013.

[36]Southern Illinois University School of Medicine. Available at: http://www.siumed.edu/pubs/A04S2.pdf. Accessed February 23, 2013.

[37]Wright State University Boonshoft School of Medicine. Available at: http://www.med.wright.edu/admiss/procedures. Accessed February 23, 2013.

[38]Delzell J. Education in Medicine Blog. Available at: http://educationinmedicine.blogspot.com/2011/03/personality-traits-that-predict-success.html. Accessed February 22, 2013.

[39]University of Wisconsin School of Medicine and Public Health. Available at: http://m.med.wisc.edu/education/md/admissions/selection-policies/111. Accessed February 22, 2013.

[40]University of South Carolina. Available at: www.sa.sc.edu/oppa/files/2011/.../Med-School-Interview-Hand-out. Accessed February 22, 2013.

[41]Kelley S, Ray M, Tsuei B. Trends concerning a common medical school interview question, revisited. *Med Teach* 2007; 29 (5): e139-42.

[42]University of Maryland School of Medicine. Available at: http://medschool.umaryland.edu/admissions/interview.asp. Accessed February 23, 2013.

[43]Davis P. Preparing for the Medical School Interview. Available at: http://web.jhu.edu/prepro/Forms/P_Davis.Med_Sch_I-view.pdf. Accessed February 23, 2013.

[44]Papadakis M, Hodgson C, Teherani A, Kohatsu N. Unprofessional behavior in medical school is associated with subsequent disciplinary action by a state medical board. *Acad Med* 2004; 79 (3): 244-9.

[45]Lowe M, Kerridge I, Bore M, Munro D, Powis D. Is it possible to assess the "ethics" of medical school applicants? *J Med Ethics* 2001; 27 (6): 404-8.

[46]Krych E, Vande Voort J. Medical students speak: a two-voice comment on learning professionalism in medicine. *Clin Anat* 2006; 19 (5): 415-8.

[47]Geisel School of Medicine at Dartmouth University. Available at: geiselmed.dartmouth.edu/faculty/pdf/admissions_committee_charge.pdf. Accessed February 22, 2013.

[48]University of Nevada School of Medicine. Available at: http://www.medicine.nevada.edu/dept/asa/students/career_prof.htm. Accessed February 22, 2013.

[49]Fatemi O. First aid for your medical school interviews. Available at: http://www.cavalierdaily.com/article/2004/10/first-aid-for-your-medical-school-interviews/. Accessed February 22, 2013.

[50]Kleshinski J, Shriner C, Khuder S. The use of professionalism scenarios in the medical school interview process: faculty and interviewee perceptions. *Med Educ Online*; 2008: 13.

[51]Rippentrop A, Wong M, Altmaier E. A content analysis of interviewee reports of medical school admissions interview. *Med Educ Online* 2003; 8.

[52]Association of American Medical Colleges. Available at: https://www.aamc.org/students/aspiring/basics/284816/interview6.html. Accessed February 23, 2013.

[53]University of Washington School of Medicine. Available at: http://www.uwmedicine.org/Education/MD-Program/Admissions/Applicants/Documents/2012-focusgroup-3-Interview.pdf. Accessed February 24, 2013.

[54]Elrakhawy M. New med school interviews ask in-depth questions. *The Daily Illini*. Available at: http://www.dailyillini.com/special_sections/archived_special_sections/article_4b17c1d1-fa22-5a7f-b3fe-9f7babeb00cc.html. Accessed February 23, 2013.

Chapter 4

Interview Preparation: The Competitive Edge

This chapter could also be titled "what applicants should always do, but often don't." The recommendations in this section are considered standard, basic interview prep for any job interview. You always research the company. You talk to any acquaintances who work at that company. You do an internet search to find out anything you can about their standard interview practices. If you know you'll be interviewing with the Vice President of Development, then you learn about her career path and her current initiatives, searching for areas that are of interest to you, as well as any areas of commonality.

These recommendations are considered standard preparation in the business world. In the world of med school admissions, though, I just don't see this level of preparation from many applicants. Your own preparation in these areas, therefore, will provide a strong competitive edge.

Rule # 15   **Research the medical school.**

As interviewers, we continue to be amazed by how many applicants come to interviews unprepared. Some have clearly done little or no research about the school. Here's how one applicant started off his interview:

"Welcome to Baylor. How's your visit so far?"

"Great. The Texas Medical Center is so amazing. I had always heard that, but you don't really get an idea of its size until you see it firsthand. I think it's great that Baylor medical students have the chance to rotate through such well-regarded hospitals. When do students rotate through MD Anderson?"

"Our students don't spend any time at MD Anderson. It's actually affiliated with the University of Texas-Houston Medical School."

"Oh, that's right. Do students do research?"

Not only did this applicant reveal a lack of knowledge about affiliated institutions, he also asked a very basic question. His question on research was clearly addressed in the school's website, and by choosing this particular question, he came across as uninformed. Dr. Christian Essman, Director of Admissions at Case Western Reserve University School of Medicine says that "coming to the school unprepared" is a common mistake. "Just like you would do for a job interview, do your homework on the school. Know what they do, how they do it, what they stand for."[1]

Prior to your visit, read all the information you've received from the school. Become familiar with both the school and its affiliated hospitals. While this data will help you ask the most informed questions, it's also vital information needed to help you evaluate the school.

These sources are helpful when researching:

- Printed materials sent from the school
- Medical Student Admission Requirements Online (MSAR Online) available at www.aamc.org
- Websites for the school and its affiliated hospitals
- Other med school applicants
- Residents and physicians who've trained at the school where you'll be interviewing
- Alumni who are current med students
- Pre-health advisors at your own university
- An internet search using the name of the school and its affiliated hospitals

Learn about the school's history, mission, philosophy, focus, curriculum, reputation, location, resources, areas of excellence, size, facilities, research, and key faculty. Schools often post their latest news on their website. Print key information to read and reread before the interview. In your research, ask "What makes this school unique?"

One highly effective approach is to obtain specific information about the school through informational interviews with current students. "Informational interview" is the formal term for a meeting where you ask questions. If you have any connection with a current med student, you can contact them. "I'll be interviewing at Baylor and I was wondering if I could call and ask you some questions about the school. It shouldn't take more than 10 minutes."

This research will help provide specific and thoughtful reasons for why you would want to attend a particular school. It also serves as the basis for the development of insightful questions. In many interviews you'll be asked "What questions do you have for me?" The best questions demonstrate your deep interest in the school, and this is one of the easiest ways to create a favorable impression.

Did you know...

Many schools offer the opportunity to stay overnight with a current med student. This can be a great way for applicants to learn more about the school, far beyond what's available on the website. However, this may not be the best approach for all applicants. Some find it more relaxing to spend the night before the interview alone.

Rule # 16   **What type of student does the medical school seek? The results of your research can help you tailor your responses.**

When researching the institution, you're also seeking information about the type of student that the school seeks. This is essential information, and you can use this knowledge to highlight the fact that you share many of the same qualities as their ideal student. [Assuming, of course, that you do. Personal integrity as well as the downfalls of insincerity are addressed elsewhere.]

For example, at the website for the Boonshoft School of Medicine at Wright State University, factors important in the selection process are described:[2]

The committee is looking for evidence of intellectual ability, dedication to human concerns, communication skills, maturity, motivation, and potential for medical service in an underserved area of Ohio.

An applicant who's spent time shadowing rural physicians could highlight this experience. Another could highlight her volunteer work for Tar Wars, which involved making presentations to elementary school students.

Admissions Officers Speak...

"Before your interview, learn as much as possible about the school. Visit the College of Medicine website to learn more about the College."[3]

Florida State University College of Medicine

"Interviewing for medical school is a lifelong job; to know nothing about the school you are interviewing at is inexcusable."[4]

Jonathan K. Muraskas, M.D. (Chairman of Medical School Admissions Committee) and Adrian Jones, M.D. (Dean of Admissions)
Loyola University Stritch School of Medicine

"Do your homework. Interviewers are generally impressed if you know something about the school you are visiting beyond what is published at their website."[5]

University of Miami Miller School of Medicine

Interview don'ts include "not knowing anything about the school or asking questions that could easily be found on the website."[6]

MedPrep Program at Washington University

Rule # 17   **Advance preparation includes researching interview format and logistics.**

Every school has an individual approach to interview sessions, and it's in your best interest to learn as much as possible about the structure, format, and logistics of your interview session.

Most schools have applicants interview with one or two admissions committee members, and the typical interview lasts about 30 to 45 minutes. Few schools require three or more interviews. However, some schools utilize formats that are substantially different.

Some schools provide very detailed information about their interview process and structure on their websites, while others offer minimal details. You can also turn to premedical advisors, current students at the school, and admissions office personnel.

Did you know...

The Student Doctor Network has a database of information about medical school interview practices based on interviewee reports.[7] The American Medical Student Association also has a database of information generated by medical students.[8]

One of the most important details to identify is the interview format used by the school. Does the school conduct standard interviews, or does it utilize a different format? Does it utilize behavioral interviews, in which specific questions are asked about prior behavior? Does it utilize group interviews, in which multiple interviewers ask questions of multiple applicants, all in one group? Some medical schools utilize the multiple-mini interview (MMI) approach, in which the applicant moves from one station to another, and is asked to respond to a short structured scenario, question, or task at each station.

In the next chapter, we'll discuss in full detail how to prepare for each of these markedly different interview formats.

What to Expect on the Interview Day

"Admissions staff and committee members will meet you in person

You will answer questions, react to scenarios, and describe your preparation and motivation to attend medical school

You will be able to visit the school and meet some faculty and students."[9]

Peggy Davis, M.D.
Director of Medical School Admissions
University of Mississippi School of Medicine

Admissions Officers Speak...

How long will the interview last?

"Candidates receive two one-to-one interviews lasting approximately 45 minutes each."[10]

Boonshoft School of Medicine at Wright State University

"You will have two one-on-one, 30 minute interviews with members of the Admissions Committee."[11]

University of Colorado School of Medicine

"Each applicant has one 45-60 minute personal interview with a member of the faculty who serves on the Committee on Admissions."[12]

Boston University School of Medicine

"Following lunch, each applicant will meet individually with two Admissions Committee members for forty-five minute interviews."[13]

University of South Carolina School of Medicine

"Applicants are interviewed exclusively by members of the admissions committee. At the present time, applicants are interviewed by one committee member and the interview lasts for approximately one hour."[14]

Miller School of Medicine at the University of Miami

"Your interview will be conducted by two College of Medicine faculty members who will meet together with you for approximately 25 minutes."[15]

Carver College of Medicine at the University of Iowa

Admissions Officers Speak...

Who will interview me?

"Applicants receive one interview by a member of the basic science faculty, clinical faculty, or a selected fourth-year medical student."[16]

Georgetown University School of Medicine

"Each applicant is scheduled for two separate interviews with faculty members or deans. Both interviews will take place at Beaumont Royal Oak."[17]

Oakland University William Beaumont School of Medicine

"Applicants interview with a faculty member from the Admissions Committee and a second year medical student."[18]

Temple University School of Medicine

"You may be interviewed by a faculty member, a clinical staff member, a non-clinical staff member, or a student member. All members of the Admissions Committee serve as full voting members, including students."[19]

University of Colorado School of Medicine

"Throughout the course of the day you will have three interviews: one with a member of the admissions staff, one with a faculty member, and one with a current medical student."[20]

University of Chicago Pritzker School of Medicine

"Interviewees have three one-on-one interviews with Admissions Committee Members who may include students, faculty and/or alumni."[21]

University of Michigan Medical School

Rule # 18   **If possible, learn the names of your faculty interviewers.**

If at all possible, learn your interviewers' names prior to your visit. For names that are difficult to pronounce, master the correct pronunciation.

This is valuable advance information, because you can now start your research. Who are these individuals? Are they purely clinicians, researchers, or both? What are their areas of interest? Do their interests overlap in any way with yours?

While it takes time and effort to perform this research, it's definitely worth it. This preparation helps lower anxiety levels. You may also be able to establish a connection. If your interviewer is a graduate of your own university, you may be able to mention this during the interview. It's a fine line, though, and you never want to overdo it.

Dr. Keith Bradley, Program Director of Research Associates Program at St. Vincent's Hospital Medical Center, provides this advice: "Some schools give you the names of your interviewers before you arrive. Knowing some things about their background, especially research interests, can lead to some interesting conversation. Don't be 'pre-med, gunner, obnoxious' about it and go overboard, but a little knowledge can be very helpful. Be honest. Don't say you really have had a life-long interest in the interviewer's work on the pathophysiology of athlete's foot unless you really do."[22]

Start by exploring the medical school's website. These often list faculty bios, and you can easily read about faculty interests and backgrounds. You should also perform an internet search, as well as a literature search. Pubmed.com is a database of published medical research, and a search by author names will pull up a faculty member's medical journal publications.

Some students utilize this information to help tailor their own questions. You'd prepare different types of questions for a medical student than you would a faculty member, and you'd seek different types of information from a researcher versus a clinician-educator.

Did you know...

"The composition of the Admissions Committee is a 200 member group of active and retired clinicians, medical students, MD/PhD faculty, basic science faculty, and lay members of the community. These are the only individuals who interview candidates for the School of Medicine."[19]

University of Colorado School of Medicine

Tip # 3

The first time it happened, I was taken aback. The well-dressed applicant walked into my office, extended his hand for a firm handshake, looked me straight in the eye, and in a confident voice said "It's nice to meet you, Samir." I've had this happen several times since.

When applicants are given their interview schedule for the day, names may be included, but titles may not. Seeing "Samir Desai" and no further information, applicants have assumed that I'm a medical student. If you're not able to determine in advance who'll be interviewing you, just assume that everyone you meet is a physician. The med student will be flattered, and the faculty member won't be offended.

Admissions Officers Speak…

"The interviewers may be clinical faculty, researchers, admissions personnel, and/or medical students. Applicants should know the position of your interviewer so that they may tailor the interview. For example, an applicant would ask different questions of a medical student than they would a clinical faculty member. Or if an applicant knows that the interviewer is on the curriculum committee, they should ask pertinent questions about the curriculum."[23]

University of Delaware

Also be sure to look up the person with whom you will interview on the Admissions Committee Bios page.[24]

Washington University School of Medicine

References

[1]Tour for Diversity in Medicine. Available at: http://tour4diversity.org/application-secrets-from-a-pro/. Accessed March 1, 2013.

[2] Wright State University Boonshoft School of Medicine. Available at: http://www.med.wright.edu/admiss/faq#1. Accessed March 3, 2013.

[3]Florida State University College of Medicine. Available at: http://med.fsu.edu/?page=mdAdmissions.interview. Accessed March 3, 2013.

[4]The Medical School Admission Process: Choosing 150 Students from 10,000+ Applications. Available at: http://csh.depaul.edu/student-resources/advising-student-services/pre-health-advising/Documents/LoyolaStritchSchoolOfMedicinePresentatio.pdf. Accessed March 2, 2013.

[5]University of Miami Miller School of Medicine. Available at: http://admissions.med.miami.edu/md-programs/general-md/reapplicants. Accessed March 4, 2013.

[6]Washington University MedPrep Program. Available at: http://medprep.wustl.edu/virtual-advisor-interview. Accessed March 5, 2013.

[7]Student Doctor Network. Available at: http://studentdoctor.net/schools/school/amc/survey/26#question_overflow_112. Accessed March 3, 2013.

[8]American Medical Student Association. Available at: http://www.amsa.org/premed/medsurvey/. Accessed March 3, 2013.

[9]Davis P. Medical school interviews: pearls and pitfalls. Available at: http://www.umc.edu/uploadedFiles/UMCedu/Content/Education/Schools/Medicine/Admissions/Medical%20School%20Interview%20Pearls%20and%20Pitfalls.pdf. Accessed March 4, 2013.

[10]Wright State University Boonshoft School of Medicine. Available at: http://www.med.wright.edu/admiss/interview. Accessed March 4, 2013.

[11]University of Colorado School of Medicine. Available at: http://www.ucdenver.edu/academics/colleges/medicalschool/education/Admissions/apply/Pages/InterviewDayInformation.aspx. Accessed March 4, 2013.

[12]Boston University School of Medicine. Available at: http://www.bumc.bu.edu/admissions/applicationprocess/interviewday/. Accessed March 4, 2013.

[13]University of South Carolina School of Medicine. Available at: http://www.greenvillemed.sc.edu/interview.shtml. Accessed March 6, 2013.

[14]Miller School of Medicine at the University of Miami. Available at: http://admissions.med.miami.edu/questions/interview-questions. Accessed March 3, 2013.

[15]Carver College of Medicine at the University of Iowa. Available at: http://www.medicine.uiowa.edu/md/interview/. Accessed March 5, 2013.

[16]Georgetown University School of Medicine. Available at: http://som.georgetown.edu/73692.html. Accessed March 2, 2013.

[17]Oakland University William Beaumont School of Medicine. Available at: https://www.oakland.edu//Default.aspx?id=16523&sid=340&CWFriendlyUrl=true. Accessed March 4, 2013.

[18]Temple University School of Medicine. Available at: http://www.temple.edu/medicine/admissions/invited_for_interview.htm. Accessed March 4, 2013.

[19]University of Colorado School of Medicine. Available at: http://www.ucdenver.edu/academics/colleges/medicalschool/education/Admissions/apply/Pages/Requirements.aspx. Accessed March 4, 2013.

[20]University of Chicago Pritzker School of Medicine. Available at: http://pritzker.uchicago.edu/admissions/faq.shtml#interviewing. Accessed March 4, 2013.

[21]University of Michigan Medical School. Available at:
http://med.umich.edu/medschool/admissions/apply/interview.html. Accessed March 3, 2013.
[22]Bradley K. So…you have a medical school interview. Available at:
http://www.raprogram.org/yahoo_site_admin/assets/docs/So_You_Have_a_Medical_Sch ool_Interview.349102805.pdf. Accessed March 4, 2013.
[23]University of Delaware. Available at:
http://www.udel.edu/CSC/pdf/MedSchoolInterviews.pdf. Accessed March 3, 2013.
[24]Washington University School of Medicine. Available at:
http://medadmissions.wustl.edu/HowtoApply/selectionprocess/Pages/TheInterviewWhatt oExpect.aspx. Accessed March 3, 2013.

Chapter 5

Interview formats

Rule # 19   **Interviews may be either open or closed file. Prepare for both.**

Most applicants go into an interview believing that their interviewer has at least looked at their file. It doesn't always work that way.

Some interviewers have chosen not to look at your file in advance, and some just haven't gotten to it yet. Others have looked at it only briefly.

In other schools, it's a matter of policy. These schools don't permit access to an applicant's file until after the interview, if then. This is known as a closed file interview. In a partially open file interview, faculty may be given some information, but quantitative information such as grades and MCAT scores are not included.

Why would schools limit access to your application? The main reason is to reduce the chance of bias, either overt or subconscious.

Research has demonstrated that bias does occur when interviewers have full access to an applicant's file as opposed to no access.[1]

Did you know...

In one study, Smilen found "a strong, striking, and statistically significant correlation between interview scores and test scores when their interviewers knew these grades, with no correlation when they did not. This finding should not be particularly surprising. The halo effect is a well-known phenomenon...in which a conclusion is reached about a job applicant within the first half minute of an encounter. After that point and during the remainder of the interview, the interviewer will subconsciously discount anything that does not fit the predetermined image of the candidate. By providing interviewers with the available performance markers, this effect can be established even in advance of interview."[2]

Admissions Officers Speak...

"What types of questions should you expect? Some may ask standard bread-and-butter queries like, 'Why do you want to be a doctor?' These are more typical in blinded interviews, where the interviewer hasn't seen your application. Others may ask specific questions about your application that focus on your hobbies or academic pursuits. Consider this a golden opportunity to present yourself as a unique individual."[3]

Paul Jung, M.D.
Deputy Director at Office of the Surgeon General

Important Points about Open versus Closed File Interviews

- Some schools will inform applicants whether the interview is open or closed file well in advance of the visit.

- For schools that don't reveal this information, a review of discussion forums, (including scutwork.com) and conversations with other applicants may help. Note that interview practices may change from year to year.

- It's always best to assume that you'll have a closed file interview until proven otherwise. Even at schools that conduct open file interviews, you may encounter an interviewer who didn't have the opportunity to review your application prior to the interview.

  Some admissions committee members are clinical faculty, and they may have to cancel their interview due to patient care issues. This is a common situation, and the admissions office will assign a new interviewer, who may not have had the time to review your file.

- Always approach every interview (open or closed file) with knowledge of the key points in your background that you must convey during the interview. This ensures that you communicate important information without leaving anything out, especially with such open-ended questions as "Tell me about yourself." Never assume that the interviewer has an understanding of even the basics in your background.

- With open file interviews, assuming that the interviewer has read your application, you can expect questions about any deficiencies or weaknesses in your background.

Tip # 4

Your file may or may not be read prior to your interview. Don't annoy or make your interviewer uncomfortable by saying:

"I don't know whether you've read my application..."
"As I wrote in my personal statement..."
"You'll see that on my application..."

Rule # 20   **Prepare for the traditional interview.**

The most common interview format is the traditional one-on-one interview. With this format, you'll find yourself face to face with your interviewer. Typically, the interviewer will ask questions about your education, activities, and goals. Examples include:

- Tell me about yourself.
- What are your strengths?
- Why are you interested in our medical school?

Traditional interviews may be structured or unstructured. In an unstructured interview, the interviewer is free to ask whatever questions he feels appropriate.[4] Unstructured interviews have not been shown to be predictive of later performance in medical school, and therefore some schools have moved to a structured process. With this approach, the interviewer is instructed to ask the same questions of every applicant and then complete the same interview scoring form. An AAMC survey of admissions officers found that "64% of schools provided general guidance to interviewers about the content of the questions they should ask."[5]

Medical Students Speak...

"From what I garnered from my interview experience, it is important to be prepared to answer the obvious questions: 'Why do you want to be a physician?' and 'Why are you interested in this school?' Practicing these answers takes some of the stress away from the interview, and using appropriate anecdotes to answer them will make the interview more interesting and memorable for the interviewer."[6]

Omid Fatemi, M.D.
Department of Cardiology
Georgetown University / Washington Hospital Center

The questions you're most likely to encounter in a traditional interview are described in Chapter 9.

Rule # 21   **Past behavior may predict future behavior.**

"Tell me about a time when you displayed teamwork."
"Tell me about a time when you showed initiative."
"In your college years, how did you handle conflict? I'd like to hear about a specific example."

These types of questions, which ask for an example, are a feature of behavioral interviews. Behavioral interviewing is based on the premise that future behavior is best predicted by past behavior. By learning how an applicant handled or reacted to a particular situation in the past, the interviewer may be able to predict how he would handle that same situation in the future.

The behavioral interview was introduced and developed by Dr. Tom Janz, an industrial psychologist. Research into its validity and accuracy has shown that behavioral interviewing is more accurate than traditional interviewing in predicting who'll succeed. While more popular in the business community, medical schools may also conduct behavioral interviews. Since each question calls for a specific example, advance preparation will help.

Admissions Officers Speak...

"We adapted the business methodology for medical student interviews, asking applicants to discuss real situations they have experienced in great detail, with continuous probing," said Suzanne Rotondo, who developed the SELECT program interview at the University of South Florida College of Medicine. "These interviews get underneath applicants' 'plug-and-play' responses – they can't fake their answers, and we can find behavioral indicators that demonstrate emotional intelligence."[7]

How should you answer this type of question? Begin by describing what happened, and then detail your actions. What resulted from your actions? Most importantly, what did you learn from the experience?
You can use the acronym STAR to help you.

S – Situation (Describe the situation in detail.)
T – Task (What was the task or obstacle?)
A – Action (What action did you take?)
R – Result (What was the result?)

Examples of behavioral questions

- Tell me about a time when you worked effectively under a great deal of pressure.

- Tell me about a particularly stressful situation you encountered in college and how you handled it.

- Tell me about a time when you were forced to make an unpopular decision.

- Tell me about a time when you were disappointed in your performance.

- Tell me about a situation in which you overcame adversity.

- Tell me about a time when you had a difficult communication problem.

- Tell me about a problem you had with a classmate or professor. How did you handle it?

- Tell me about a time when you handled a stressful situation poorly.

- Tell me about a time when you became really angry over a situation in college.

- Describe to me a situation in which you had to break someone's confidence.

- Tell me about a time when you witnessed unprofessional or unethical behavior on the part of a classmate. How did you handle it?

- Tell me about a time when you had to build rapport quickly with someone under difficult conditions.

- Tell me about a difficult decision you've made in the last year.

- Tell me about the major challenges you've faced in your college career.

- Give me an example of a time when you motivated others.

- Give me an example of when you showed initiative and took the lead.

- Tell me about a time when you were able to successfully work with another person, even when you didn't like them personally.

- Tell me about a time when others working with you disagreed with your ideas. How did you handle it?

- Tell me about a time when you had to go above and beyond the call of duty in order to get a job done.

- Describe a situation that required a number of things to be done at the same time. How did you handle it? What was the result?

- Tell me about a time when you put your needs aside to help a classmate or coworker understand a task. How did you help him or her? What was the result?

- Describe a situation in which your performance did not meet your professor's or supervisor's expectations. What happened? How did you handle the situation?

Rule # 22   The conversational interview can be dangerous.

"That didn't feel like an interview. It was just a normal conversation."

We've heard many applicants say something to this effect following an interview. If you leave an interview feeling this way, you've likely taken part in what is termed a conversational interview. In this type, the interviewer does not have a list of prepared questions. The next question is often based on a point you just made.

The goal of the conversational interview is to put you at ease and build rapport in an effort to learn more about you as a person. The trained interviewer has a certain agenda in mind, knows what information he seeks, and has decided that a conversational interview is the best way to elicit this information. The interview quickly becomes a chat. With this type of interview, you can't become too relaxed, or you may reveal items you wouldn't have in a traditional interview.

Assuming that you don't drop your guard, having an engaging conversation with a trained interviewer is generally to your advantage. "Remember the ideal interview is a *conversation*," writes Sylvia Robertson, Assistant Dean for Admissions at the Pritzker School of Medicine at the University of Chicago. "There is nothing more frustrating for an interviewer than talking with a candidate who is simply responding to specific questions with general, rehearsed answers. Engage in the conversation and enjoy the opportunity to discuss your vision and goals."[8]

Don't be surprised if your interviewer spends considerable time talking about one of your interests. You may find yourself in a conversation about cooking, hiking, biking, or travel. While fun, you may feel the need to redirect the interviewer to what's most important in your mind – your qualifications that make you a great candidate at that school. After all, you've prepared winning responses to interview questions. However, it's very important to not force the issue. Some very seasoned interviewers prefer their approach.

If you feel that you've been unable to convey key points, one approach would be to share this information when the interviewer asks, "Do you have any questions?" You can respond by saying, "Before I ask you a few questions, I wonder if I can share a few more things about..." At this point in the interview, though, always be brief. This question typically serves as a signal that the interview is ending.

Rule # 23   Panel interviews may be used to gauge your composure and ability to deal with a stressful situation.

In a panel interview, you'll be interviewed by two or more interviewers simultaneously. Panel interviews allow the school to assess your composure, your ability to deal with stressful situations, and your interactions with different people. Through the use of panel interviews, schools can expose more members of their selection committee to applicants, which provides additional judgments. This can allow for a more productive discussion of each candidate at the admissions committee meeting.

Although panel interviews may seem more intimidating, your preparation will essentially be the same as it would for a one-on-one interview. Don't let the fact that you're outnumbered affect your poise, confidence, and your ability to sell yourself.

Tips for Success in a Panel Interview

- Be clear on the interviewers' names and, from time to time, use them during the interview.

- Direct your response initially to the interviewer who asked the question.

- Try to position yourself so that you can see all members of the panel without having to move your head from one side to another. Constant head movement can be stressful, and will appear distracting.

- As you delve further into your answer, make eye contact with the other interviewers.

- Do not dart your eyes from one interviewer to another. Instead make eye contact, pause briefly on each, and then move on to the next panel member.

- As you conclude your response, make eye contact once again with the interviewer who asked the question.

- Don't be alarmed if one or more interviewers show little to no expression or enthusiasm. Continue your efforts to sell yourself, and don't let their lack of emotion dampen the enthusiasm of your response.

- Often, one of the panel members will take the lead in asking questions. The natural response may be to focus on this individual. However, your goal is to establish rapport with all interviewers.

- Sometimes, a panel interview may turn into a conversation between the interviewers themselves. With this scenario, an applicant loses the chance to make an impression. Should this happen, don't hesitate to insert yourself into the conversation in a tactful manner. "Would this be a good time for me to talk about…"

Rule # 24   **The group interview calls for a different approach.**

The Feinberg School of Medicine at Northwestern University utilizes a group approach, in which multiple interviewers speak with multiple applicants in one group. The format is based on the school's small-group, interactive, problem-based learning curriculum. The school describes its approach below:[9]

Two medical school faculty members and a fourth-year medical student, serve as interviewers. Three to four candidates are interviewed together for one hour and fifteen minutes. The interview is conducted 'blind' which means that the interviewers have not reviewed the candidates' application. During the interview, the interviewers ask questions and observe applicants to assess personal characteristics such as maturity, professionalism, empathy, and interpersonal skills, including cooperativeness, oral expression, and attention to others. Interviewers also ask questions to determine each candidate's motivation for and knowledge concerning a career in medicine. Problem-solving skills are evaluated during a collaborative group activity.

Admissions Officers Speak...

Medical schools which don't conduct group interviews may still be very interested in how you interact with other applicants. "...we have a collaborative environment and we want our students to be able to work well in groups together and to be friendly with each other, if you are simply sitting by yourself reading a book or working a crossword puzzle or whatever it might be during the entire day while other applicants are around you chatting and conversing and kind of hanging out with each other, it causes us to question to a degree are you somebody who likes to work on teams? Are you somebody who likes to be collaborative?"[10]

Joni Krapec
Director of Admissions & Outreach
Pritzker School of Medicine at the University of Chicago

Important Points about Group Interviews[11]

A group interview should be viewed as a small group discussion with faculty. To prepare effectively, you first have to learn what qualities are considered important when evaluating a student in any type of small group setting. The following information is based on a study examining the expectations of faculty members for students in small group settings.

- In the study, faculty identified the qualities of an ideal student. These included:

  - Participates and contributes to discussions
  - Helps other classmates
  - Is not intimidated by questions
  - Voices opinions
  - Listens attentively to classmates
  - Is serious about the group process and the material discussed

- Problem students were divided into three types:

  - The nonparticipating, quiet, and passive student
  - The disruptive student who is sarcastic, disrespectful, or interrupts discussions
  - The student who tries to take over the group and control it

- Also viewed poorly were students who didn't take the group's efforts seriously and were uninterested in group activities or in their fellow students. "Show offs" and "competitive" students were also viewed unfavorably.

Blue AV, Elam C, Fosson S, Bonaminio G. Faculty members' expectations of student behavior in the small-group setting. *Med Educ Online* 1998; 3: 5.

Rule # 25   **Although stress interviews are no longer common, this format may still be used by some faculty members.**

The purpose of the stress interview is to assess your response and composure following the use of tactics that are specifically designed to create stress. Although stress interviews have largely fallen out of favor in the admissions process, some interviewers may still be proponents. Dr. Steven Hausrath, a former member of the admissions committee at the University of Texas Medical Branch at Galveston, offered his experiences with the stress interview during a lecture given at SUNY Plattsburgh:[12]

There are stress interviews — we're taught how to give an interview to put some people under stress. Why is that? Because how one reacts to stress is very stereotyped. One reacts to stress in the same way whether it's traffic, a money problem, or whether it's a dilemma at work or in the laboratory. So by provoking a stress response in someone, you get a sense of how they're going to approach a problem or a hurdle. If they become unglued, then that's not a good thing.

How can you tell if you're participating in a stress interview? Clues include:

- Confrontational questions
- Inappropriate or challenging questions
- Repeatedly being asked "Why" questions
- Seemingly disinterested interviewer
- Rude or sarcastic interviewer
- Jumping all over you no matter what you say
- Deliberate and prolonged silence following your answer
- Criticism of your academic record, MCAT scores, or involvement in extracurricular activities, community service, or medically-related activities
- Rapid fire questions from several interviewers at the same time

The key to success in this type of interview is recognizing what's occurring. As uncomfortable as this may be, don't view it as a personal attack. No matter how the interviewer chooses to "stress" you, hold your emotions in check. Remain calm and composed, listen carefully to each question, and respond appropriately, without emotion.

"I want a medical school applicant to discuss difficult issues with me calmly, rationally, thoughtfully, and humbly - and to be respectful and polite even if I disagree with them and even if I test them by being rude and argumentative," writes Dr. David H. Blatt. "You will need these skills when you become a doctor. These skills will enable you to deal with almost any issue you might face during your medical career."[13]

Medical Students Speak...

"On my first medical school interview I sat patiently with my fellow applicants waiting for our impending interviews. The room felt tense as we thought about the types of questions we would be asked to clarify our various academic attributes: What type of research did you do? Why did you pick your major? Why do you want to come to this medical school? After several minutes of waiting, the dean of admissions entered the room holding three stress balls. 'Which one of you is Alex?' she asked. Alex, confused, slowly raised his hand. The dean tossed Alex the three balls. 'Your application said that you're a fire juggler. That's awesome! Show us.'"[14]

Admissions Officers Speak...

"During the interview season, applicants might be taking planes and trains to interview visits, experiencing jet lag, struggling to manage their academic obligations back in school, and trying to get enough sleep so that they are at their best in the interviews. At Yale, we try to minimize stress by making the interview day as relaxing as it can be, but we know that applicants will be nervous and excited, and that's perfectly okay."[15]

Richard Silverman
Director of Admissions at Yale University School of Medicine

Tips to Handle the Stress Interview

- Remember that the stress interview is designed to determine how well you perform under pressure.

- Remember that the stress interview is an act. Therefore it's not a personal attack, and you shouldn't view it as such.

- Hold your emotions in check. Remain calm and composed.

- Listen carefully to each question, and ask for clarification if necessary.

- Avoid rushing into your response. Don't be afraid to pause for a few seconds to gather your thoughts.

- Be aware of the tone of your voice. Don't match your interviewer's tone.

- Answer the question calmly and confidently, without being defensive or argumentative.

Rule # 26   Review the types of scenarios and tasks that may be used in the MMI (multiple mini-interview).

"Our school intends to graduate physicians who can communicate with patients and work in a team. So if people do poorly on the MMI, they will not be offered positions in our class."[16]

> Dr. Cynda Ann Johnson
> Dean of the Virginia Tech Carilion School of Medicine

What is the MMI? What are the chances that you'll have to face it? Some medical schools have opted to replace the traditional interview with the multiple mini-interview (MMI) approach developed by the McMaster University School of Medicine in 2002. During the MMI, the interviewee moves from one station to another over a two-hour period. At each station, the interviewee is asked to respond to a short structured scenario, question, or task. Trained raters are present to observe and score the candidate's performance.

Why have schools adopted this new interview approach? Studies of the traditional interview have found that interview ratings are significantly influenced by the biases, expectations, and perspectives of the individual interviewers. While variance in interview ratings is multifactorial, research has shown that interviewer variability is a major factor, accounting for 56% of the variance in interview scores.[17] By using a structured and consistent approach with multiple raters, the MMI has been shown to be reliable and possibly predictive of future performance in medical school. "We adopted the MMI approach to explore a potentially more reliable, multisource assessment of our applicants than the traditional, one-on-one interview format," said Dr. Mark Henderson, Associate Dean for Admissions at the UC Davis School of Medicine.[18]

The specific scenarios vary from school to school, depending on which attributes the med school has determined are important to assess. Once these attributes are determined, stations can be designed to test for them. Of note, these interviews are not a test of scientific knowledge. "The stations deal with a variety of issues, which may include but are not limited to, communication, collaboration, ethics, health policy, critical thinking, awareness of society health issues in Canada and personal qualities," writes McMaster University.[19]

"The multiple mini-interview allows for a more objective approach and provides the candidate a fair evaluation if he doesn't particularly 'click' with an interviewer," said Chris Dougherty, a medical student at the University of Calgary.[20] In fact, research indicates that most applicants prefer the MMI. In a study of interviewees' opinions about the MMI, researchers found that applicants considered the MMI to be fair and effective, rating it more highly than the traditional interview. However, candidates did feel that the MMI was more stressful than the traditional interview.[21]

The MMI has been increasingly utilized by med schools. The next sections quote admissions directors from medical schools across the country, indicating the diversity of schools utilizing this same structured approach.

Important Points about the Multiple Mini-Interview (MMI)

- Research the school's interview practices to determine if you'll be participating in a multiple mini-interview.

- The typical MMI involves 8 to 10 stations.

- You'll be presented with various scenarios, usually posted on the door.

- You'll have 2 minutes to read the scenario.

- You may or may not be able to take notes.

- You'll then be prompted to enter the room, where you will respond to the scenario, task, or question.

- Following your initial answer, the interviewer may provide you with new information, probe you further with follow-up questions, or disagree with your perspective. A large part of your interview score will be based on how you handle this portion of the scenario. Do you listen well? Do you ask for more information? Are you open to receiving new information? Do you jump to conclusions, or do you approach the issue logically? Do you offer reasons to substantiate your viewpoint? How do you respond to disagreement?

- Recognizing one's limitations is a mark of a good physician. Feel free to state that you would seek the input of colleagues, medical ethics boards, or other sources to help you reach a decision.

- Another prompt will indicate the end of the encounter.

- Don't let what you believe to be a poor performance at one station affect your performance at other stations. Applicants aren't usually the best judges of their own performance. Even if you didn't do well at a single station, you have multiple stations which offer the chance to improve your overall rating.

- After your interview, document your experiences, including scenarios. These same scenarios may be used at the next school. While you can use these to improve your own performance, you cannot share this information. In fact, some schools have applicants sign a nondisclosure form.

MMI Examples

Stanford University

Scenario # 1 (Teamwork Scenario) – "Two applicants participate in a scenario in which one applicant is asked to perform a complex test (such as assembling or repairing a model) with the other applicant giving directions for dealing with or assembling the model. In this scenario, the raters observe the communication and teamwork of the applicants."[22]

Scenario # 2 (Ethical Decision Making Scenario) – "The applicant is given the following statement to read over 2 minutes before entering the room: 'Recently in Congress, there has been a discussion concerning the issue of deterrent fees for all individuals on either Medicare or Medicaid (a small charge, say $20, which everyone who initiates a visit to a health professional would have to pay for every contact) as a way to control health care costs.' The assumption is that this will deter people from visiting their doctor for unnecessary reasons. Consider the broad implications of this policy for health and health care costs. For example, do you think the approach will save health care costs? At what expense?"[22]

Examples from Eva et al

Scenario # 1 (Placebo [Ethical Decision Making]) – "Dr. Cheung recommends homeopathic medicines to his patients. There is no scientific evidence or widely accepted theory to suggest that homeopathic medicines work, and Dr. Cheung doesn't believe them to. He recommends homeopathic medicine to people with mild and non-specific symptoms such as fatigue, headaches and muscle aches, because he believes that it will do no harm, but will give them reassurance. Consider the ethical problems that Dr. Cheung's behavior might pose. Discuss these issues with the interviewer."[23]

Scenario # 2 (Parking Garage [Communication Skills]) – "The parking garage at your place of work has assigned parking spots. On leaving your spot, you are observed by the garage attendant as you back into a neighboring car, a BMW, knocking out its left front headlight and denting the left front fender. The garage attendant gives you the name and office number of the owner of the neighboring car, telling you that he is calling ahead to the car owner, Tim. The garage attendant tells you that Tim is expecting your visit. Enter Tim's office."[23]

Eva K, Rosenfeld J, Reiter H, Normal G. An admissions OSCE: the multiple mini-interview. *Med Educ* 2004; 38 (3): 314-26.

Additional MMI examples available at the University of Calgary website[24]

Admissions Officers Speak...

"The MMI allows for a broad view of an applicant. Because the raters haven't seen the student's files, they are simply evaluating interpersonal skills, the ability to communicate clearly, to reason, to be empathic, and so on. In the end, we have the perspective of 8 to 10 people with no prior knowledge of the student. That's a valuable supplement to the student's file."[25]

Charles Prober, M.D.
Senior Associate Dean for Medical Education
Stanford University School of Medicine

"GPA and MCAT scores are good indicators of student performance in the first and second years of medical school when the basic sciences are the major focus. But when students are involved in direct patient care in the third year, interpersonal skills, communication, professionalism, cultural competency, and teamwork are paramount. The MMI is the first tool that has been shown to have predictive validity for these competencies and overall performance in the clinical years."[26]

Fern R. Juster, M.D.
Senior Associate Dean for Admissions at New York Medical College

----

"MMIs are a series of 7-minute stations that 'test' attributes and/or traits sought in a medical student: interpersonal communication, teamwork, ethical and moral judgment, etc. Each station is guided by a 'rater' who interacts with the applicant by asking a series of follow-up questions, building on the initial prompt or situation that the student spent 2-minutes preparing a response. MMIs are not a debate or oratory contest, rather a structured interview occurring 10 times around different questions...Each interview process should be daunting in that you cannot fully anticipate what kinds of questions you will be asked, nor should you try to have a response ready. MMIs are not designed to test 'medical knowledge' or any other discipline, for that matter. MMIs are designed to elicit new information or 'data' about an applicant."[27]

Tara Cunningham
Executive Director for the Office of Admissions and Recruitment
University of Arizona College of Medicine – Phoenix

"Attributes that enhance team-based health care, like communication skills, comfort with mutual decision-making and respect for other health professions will be increasingly important. The MMI process will help in our ongoing goal to always be educating the types of physicians most needed by society."[28]

Mark Richardson, M.D.
Dean
Oregon Health Sciences University School of Medicine.

"Since we've been using MMI, it's been very enlightening, because it allows you to see the candidate in a different venue, where they're actually dealing with clinical scenarios and you can measure different types of behavior that might not be immediately evident. I think it helps identify the type of student that would be the best fit for this institution, encompassing the mission that the university has -- caring, compassionate, lifelong learners. This way you're seeing this other side of them that you cannot adequately assess on the paper application."[29]

Marian Safaoui, M.D.
Assistant Professor of Anatomy and Surgery
College of Osteopathic Medicine of the Pacific

"The overarching purpose of the MMI is to measure communication, critical thinking and teamwork skills. One of our MMI interview stations asks applicants to 'role play' by acting out a scenario with a trained actor; this allows our MMI raters to see how an applicant reacts to and resolves a particular scenario. We also use a scenario that requires applicants to work together to solve a problem or issue. Because physicians need good communication, critical thinking, and teamwork skills, we are very interested in evaluating these characteristics in our applicants."[30]

Steve Manuel, Ph.D.
Assistant Dean of Admissions at the University of Cincinnati College of Medicine

----

"The strongest advice is to understand the basic structure, time limit, and number of stations. Listen carefully to any prompts directed to you. Reviewing a list of 'practice' questions is not helpful because the MMI does not use the same questions as you experience during a traditional interview. As with any other human interaction, practice is helpful because it might identify nervous habits and also help you feel more comfortable and relaxed."[31]

Duke University School of Medicine

"An applicant's disappointing performance in one MMI station doesn't carry the same weight as with the traditional interview. He or she has nine other stations in which to do well."[32]

Francis Sousa, M.D.
Member of the Admissions Committee
University of California Davis School of Medicine

References

[1]Robin A, Bombeck C, Pollak R, Nyhus L. Introduction of bias in residency-candidate interviews. *Surgery* 1991; 110 (2): 253-8.

[2]Smilen S, Funai E, Bianco A. Residency selection: should interviewers be given applicant's board scores. *Am J Obstet Gynecol* 2001; 184 (3): 508-13.

[3]American Medical Student Association. Available at: http://www.amsa.org/AMSA/Homepage/MemberCenter/Premeds/PremedRx.aspx. Accessed March 3, 2013.

[4]Johnson E, Edwards J. Current practices in admissions interviews at U. S. medical schools. *Acad Med* 1991; 66: 408-12.

[5]Dunleavy D, Whittaker K. The evolving medical school admissions interview. *AIB* 2011: 11 (7).

[6]Fatemi O. First aid for your medical school interviews. Available at: http://www.cavalierdaily.com/article/2004/10/first-aid-for-your-medical-school-interviews/. Accessed February 22, 2013.

[7]University of South Florida College of Medicine. Available at: http://health.usf.edu/nocms/publicaffairs/now/pdfs/AAMCReporter_SELECT.pdf. Accessed March 4, 2013.

[8]University of Chicago Health Professions Handbook, the Office of the Dean of Students in the College, and the Newsletter of the Central Association of Advisors for the Health Professions. Available at: http://web.jhu.edu/prepro/health/Applicants/interviewing.html. Accessed February 22, 2013.

[9]Northwestern University Feinberg School of Medicine. Available at: http://www.feinberg.northwestern.edu/admissions/process/interview.html. Accessed March 4, 2013.

[10]Pritzker School of Medicine at the University of Chicago. Available at: http://pritzkerpodcast.com/2010/01/11/26-interview-tips-mp3/#more-557. Accessed March 4, 2013.

[11]Blue A, Elam C, Fosson S, Bonaminio G. Faculty members' expectations of student behavior in the small-group setting. *Med Educ Online* 1998; 3: 5.

[12]SUNY Plattsburgh. Available at: http://www.plattsburgh.edu/academics/prehealthadvising/insiderhausrath.php. Accessed March 3, 2013.

[13]Blatt D. Preparing for your medical school interview. Available at: http://www.science.oregonstate.edu/files/science/premed_interview_prep.pdf. Accessed March 4, 2013.

[14]Greene A, Bailey C. Juggling academic ability and cultural curiosity. Available at: http://www.internetandpsychiatry.com/joomla/home-page/editorials-and-commentaries/698-juggling-academic-ability-and-cultural-curiosity.html. Accessed March 3, 2013.

[15]Balakrishna K. Med school hopefuls face up to interview pressures. *Yale Daily News.* Available at: http://yaledailynews.com/blog/2006/09/27/med-school-hopefuls-face-up-to-interview-pressures/. Accessed March 3, 2013.

[16]Gardiner H. New for aspiring doctors, the people skills test. *New York Times.* Available at: http://www.nytimes.com/2011/07/11/health/policy/11docs.html?pagewanted=all&_r=0. Accessed March 3, 2013.

[17]Harasym PH, Woloschuk W, Mandin H, Brundin-Mather R, Reliability and validity of interviewers' judgments of medical school candidates. *Acad Med* 1996; 71: 40s-42s.

[18]University of California Davis School of Medicine. Available at: http://www.ucdmc.ucdavis.edu/publish/news/newsroom/6802. Accessed March 4, 2013.

[19]McMaster University Faculty of Medicine. Available at: http://fhs.mcmaster.ca/mdprog/interviews.html. Accessed March 3, 2013.

[20]Watson R. Mini-interviews make impression. University of Calgary *OnCampus Weekly*. Available at: http://www.ucalgary.ca/oncampus/weekly/april7-06/mini-interviews.html. Accessed March 3, 2013.

[21]Razack S, Faremo S, Drolet F, Snell L, Wiseman J, Pickering J. Multiple mini-interviews versus traditional interviews: stakeholder acceptability comparison. *Med Educ* 2009; 43 (10): 993-1000.

[22]Stanford University School of Medicine. Available at: http://deansnewsletter.stanford.edu/archive/11_08_10.html#4. Accessed March 3, 2013.

[23]Eva K, Rosenfeld J, Reiter H, Normal G. An admissions OSCE: the multiple mini-interview. *Med Educ* 2004; 38 (3): 314-26.

[24]University of Calgary. Available at: http://www.ucalgary.ca/mdprogram/files/mdprogram/2008_09%20MMI%20Cases.pdf. Accessed March 23, 2013.

[25]Stanford University School of Medicine. Available at: http://med.stanford.edu/alumni/magazine/nov2011/feature2.html. Accessed March 2, 2013.

[26]New York Medical College. Available at: http://www.nymc.edu/OfficesAndServices/PublicRelations/Assets/June2012_InTouch.pdf. Accessed March 3, 2013.

[27]University of Arizona College of Medicine – Phoenix. Available at: http://alumni.medicine.arizona.edu/newsletterstory/tucson-admissions-elects-new-interview-technique. Accessed March 3, 2013.

[28]Oregon Health Sciences University. Available at: http://www.ohsu.edu/xd/education/schools/school-of-medicine/about/school-of-medicine-news/education-news/multiple-mini-interviews-4111.cfm. Accessed March 3, 2013.

[29]College of Osteopathic Medicine of the Pacific. Available at: http://wsprod.westernu.edu/news/nr_detail.jsp?id=13243. Accessed March 5, 2013.

[30]University of Cincinnati College of Medicine. Available at: http://www.ucphysicians.com/wp-content/uploads/2010/09/Connected_August2011_FINAL.pdf. Accessed March 3, 2013.

[31]Duke University School of Medicine. Available at: http://dukemed.duke.edu/modules/ooa_applicant/index.php?id=9. Accessed March 3, 2013.

[32]University of California Davis School of Medicine. Available at: http://www.ucdmc.ucdavis.edu/facultydev/pdfs/FacDevNLDec10_Jan11_pages.pdf. Accessed March 4, 2013.

Chapter 6

Interview preparation: The Basics

Rule # 27   Medical schools consider communication to be a vital skill, and will evaluate your proficiency during the interview.

"We are trying to weed out the students who look great on paper but haven't developed the people or communication skills we think are important," said Dr. Stephen Workman, Associate Dean for Admissions at the Carilion School of Medicine at Virginia Tech University.[1] "Candidates who jump to improper conclusions, fail to listen or are overly opinionated fare poorly because such behavior undermines teams. Those who respond appropriately to the emotional tenor of the interviewer or ask for more information do well in the new admissions process because such tendencies are helpful not only with colleagues but also with patients."

If you think about your encounters with doctors, either as a patient or through shadowing, you know that the basis of every physician – patient encounter is a symptom or concern.

To establish the diagnosis, the physician must start by listening carefully and effectively to the patient's story. He then has to ask insightful questions to elicit key information. He must be able to explain even complex diagnoses in terms that are easily understood by the patient. He also has to communicate a treatment plan, and he has to ensure that the patient understands and is able to comply with the recommendations.

"Communication skills are important, not only for physicians in their consultations with patients and their families, but also in their contacts with all members of the health care team," writes Dr. Carol Elam, Associate Dean for Admissions at the University of Kentucky College of Medicine.[2]

Given the importance of communication skills in the practice of medicine, medical schools routinely assess for these skills in the admissions interview. In a recent survey of admissions officers, oral communication was assessed at the time of the interview by 91% of schools.[6]

In assessing your communication skills, interviewers seek to answer some very important questions. Are you a good listener? How well do you express yourself? Can you easily engage in conversation? Do you connect with people? The answers to these questions help the interviewer answer the most important question of all: If I were a patient, how would I feel if this person in front of me was my doctor?

Admissions Officers Speak...

"Specifically, the interviewers will try to determine the following:

What has motivated you to pursue a career in medicine?
How well do you communicate with others? (This includes listening skills as well as skills in transmitting information to others)."[3]

University of Washington School of Medicine

"A physician must not only be able to speak effectively with a patient, but must be able to listen effectively and ask good questions. It is important to be able to balance these speaking and listening skills so that information is transmitted in an accurate and efficient manner...Interviewers are particularly sensitive to applicants who are too verbose, fail to answer the questions directly, or who dominate the conversation without asking any questions. The Committee on Admissions encourages students to practice their interview with their colleagues and teachers. Applicants should pay attention to body language and refrain from nervous habits. Many applicants with outstanding academic credentials and a wealth of clinical and volunteer activities fail to gain entrance to the School of Medicine due to poor interviews."[4]

University of New Mexico School of Medicine

"Essential interpersonal and communication skills for physicians include the ability to listen effectively, communicate concisely and accurately orally and in writing...The Committee looks for applicants who have demonstrated behaviors consistent with these skills and abilities. Students who are successful in medical school have demonstrated these abilities in their undergraduate and premedical school experiences."[5]

University of Alabama School of Medicine

"The single most common mistake is failure to answer the question."[6]

University of Mississippi School of Medicine

Rule # 28   **Plan to convey a message with every response you provide.**

In preparing answers for potential interview questions, begin by jotting down the key points you'd like to convey for each question. Then rehearse. Your goal is not to deliver a perfectly worded response every time, but rather to ensure that your responses convey the correct message.

Don't take this to mean that you should memorize your answers, because sometimes that can be worse than an "I don't know." Some candidates produce canned responses, and some become easily flustered and very anxious when they can't remember a specific point or line they had planned to say.

The point of preparation is rather to ensure that you convey your key points in every response. Some examples:

Why are you interested in coming to Baylor?

I plan to include these key points in my response: early patient exposure, opportunity to participate in different tracks (international health, care for the underserved, medical research), increased elective time, diversity of patient population from rotations at multiple affiliated institutions

Why do you want to be a doctor?

Tell story of my shadowing experiences, explain my interest in patient education, go over my medical and teaching experiences so far

---

Medical Student Speaks...

"From what I garnered from my interview experience, it is important to be prepared to answer the obvious questions: "Why do you want to be a physician?" and "Why are you interested in this school?" Practicing these answers takes some of the stress away from the interview, and using appropriate anecdotes to answer them will make the interview more interesting and memorable for the interviewer."[7]

Omid Fatemi, M.D.
Department of Cardiology
Georgetown University / Washington Hospital Center

Admissions Officers Speak...

"It's important to have key points you can get across during the interview. But you don't want to sound too rehearsed or mechanical, even if you are talking about something you've gone over a thousand times."[8]

Gregory Goldmacher, M.D., Ph.D.

"Remember the ideal interview is a conversation. There is nothing more frustrating for an interviewer than talking with a candidate who is simply responding to specific questions with general, rehearsed answers. Engage in the conversation and enjoy the opportunity to discuss your vision and goals."[9]

Sylvia Robertson
Assistant Dean for Admissions and Financial Aid
Pritzker School of Medicine at the University of Chicago

"I interviewed several applicants at Dartmouth who were rock stars on paper but in person were boring, without personality, not willing or able to talk openly or to share their opinions and views...Many of us apply what we call 'the mommy test' in admissions interviews. We ask ourselves, 'Would I want to bring my sick mother to this person for medical care?' Communication with patients and their families is part and parcel of being a physician. If you can't talk and use emotion and listen and respond, you lack a key ingredient for being a good physician. Your interview is your chance to show you can do those things."[8]

Mark Edney, M.D.
Former Admissions Committee Member
Geisel School of Medicine at Dartmouth University

Rule # 29   **Every element of your medical school application is up for discussion. Know it cold.**

Prior to each interview, review every element of your med school application. Anything in your application is fair game for an interviewer. For each line in your application, ask yourself these questions: Would an interviewer ask about this item? What would he ask? How would you respond?

     If you've listed a semester spent in a study abroad program, an interviewer may ask how that experience shaped your commitment to medicine. If you wrote about tutoring high school students, you may be asked what you found most difficult about the experience. If you described your research experience, many interviewers will ask for more details.

Jordana spoke eloquently about her research during her med school interview. Her project took place over two years during her undergraduate years. In describing her role in the project, she spoke with great enthusiasm and energy. The interviewer then asked, "Which journal was your work published in?" Jordana couldn't remember, stammering "I'm blanking on the journal but I believe I have it here somewhere." She fumbled through her portfolio, finally saying, "I think it was in Vaccine."

"The most frequently asked MD interview question was for me a question about my application, either something I said in an essay, or details about my involvement with an extracurricular thing I put down," writes Dr. Michael Greger.[47]

Admissions Officers Speak...

"Make sure that whatever research or other experience you have had, you know it cold – otherwise you lose your credibility. Be prepared to answer questions about yourself and your experiences."[10]

Dr. Judith Amorosa
Program Director of the Radiology Residency Program
UMDNJ/Robert Wood Johnson Medical School

"It is especially important to be prepared to talk about ANYTHING on your application and explain and elaborate on it. Try to make it exciting when you are talking to an interviewer."[11]

Lisa Cifelli, Academic Director of Admissions, Drexel University College of Medicine

Rule # 30   **Prepare to address the red flags in your application.**

Some applicants have obvious weaknesses in their applications, which are typically viewed as negatives. Should these be addressed in the interview? How?

Potential red flags:

- Low grades
- Low MCAT scores
- Leave of absence
- Issues with professionalism
- Institutional action
- Significant time gaps

Red flags are difficult to discuss. If you can address the issue successfully, and allay any concerns, you have the chance to secure a strong advocate in the admissions process.

To address a negative, follow these guidelines:

- Address the negative or weakness in a careful, matter-of-fact manner. Don't dwell on the weakness.
- Discuss the reasons that led to the red flag. If you had a lower GPA in college, an explanation of the contributing factors may help alleviate the concern that you wouldn't be able to keep up in medical school. Such factors may include health issues, family issues, financial problems, or others.
- Offer the explanation without making any excuses. Don't whine or complain, and definitely don't blame any other individuals, departments, or institutions.
- Explain what you learned from the experience, how it will help you in the future, and why it's unlikely to occur again.

"What did you find to be the most challenging aspect of your undergrad experience?"

"I'd have to say my freshman semester. Unfortunately, the workload took me by surprise, and my first semester grades reflected this. However, ultimately the experience served me well. I attended several workshops on study skills, read about the subject, and honed my approach to an intense workload. While my first semester grades impacted my overall GPA, I learned enough from the experience that I made the Dean's list in every single following semester."

Tip # 5

Are there any areas of concern that might come up during the interview? If so, decide in advance how you'll handle any related questions.

Tip # 6

In an open file interview, the interviewer is likely to raise the red flag issue himself. If he doesn't, it may be in your best interests to bring it up yourself. This allows you to shape the discussion and the story. At some point, the interviewer will present your candidacy to the admissions committee. Your answers during an interview can ultimately shape and guide that discussion.

Did you know…

"If you have an incident on your record, but have made it to the interview , you have surmised that checking 'yes' on the institutional action section of the AMCAS did not instantly veto your application. If this is brought up during the interview it is important to address this issue in a forthright manner because it would be worse to be caught in a lie than to report your youthful indiscretions. This description needs to include the offense, the context in which it happened and how it was handled. Most importantly the student needs to demonstrate what they learned from this experience and how they have grown and changed for the better because of it."

Brian Clinton
Biological Sciences Advisor
University of Rhode Island

Handling Red Flags in Your Application During the Interview

Low GPA

If you've been invited to an interview, rest assured that the school has assessed your academic credentials and decided that you have the ability to handle the academic challenges of medical school. However, they may seek an explanation for any poor grades or academic difficulties. Schools need to know that the issues that led to your academic difficulties won't impact your medical school performance.

Did you have a health issue? Was there a family illness or emergency? Did you experience some type of personal challenge? Be honest in offering your explanation. If your poor academic performance was due to a lack of focus or immaturity, it's best to disclose this and provide evidence to indicate that that issue is now resolved. Never blame the school or its curriculum.

Low MCAT score

The MCAT score has been shown to have value in predicting performance during the basic science years and on medical school standardized exams. Your score is therefore of obvious importance to medical schools. If you feel that your score is on the low side, be ready to address this in the interview. Since applicants are allowed to retake the MCAT as often as they would like, it can be difficult to offer a compelling reason as to why you were unable to achieve a higher score.

The best approach is to provide the interviewer with other evidence of your academic ability and competency. Examples would include your high overall or science undergraduate GPA or stellar academic performance in graduate study.

Lack of extracurricular activities, particularly service or medically-related experiences

It would be unusual for an applicant with no involvement in outside activities to receive an interview invitation. However, some applicants may have a relative lack of certain types of activities, be it community service or activities providing exposure to the medical field. The recommended approach here, if you lack a breadth of involvement, is to effectively describe the depth of your involvement. It's helpful to describe the meaningful contributions you made, and what your involvement reveals about your personality.

Institutional action / criminal offense

Being disciplined for institutional misconduct, or even having a criminal record, is not grounds for automatic rejection of your application. It's still possible for you to receive an interview. The University of North Carolina asks on their Supplemental Application "Have you ever entered a plea of guilty, a plea of no contest...to a criminal charge?" They also ask "Have you ever been expelled, dismissed, suspended, placed on probation, or otherwise subject to any disciplinary sanction by any school, college, or university?"[12]

"Your 'yes' answer to one or more of these questions will not necessarily preclude your being admitted," writes the university. Of key importance is how you handle inquiries about the issue during the interview. "This will allow them to make an informed decision regarding your suitability as a medical student, and eventually, as a practicing physician," writes the University of Maryland School of Medicine.[13]

Rule # 31   **Always prepare with a mock interview.**

Practice, practice, practice. We can't emphasize this rule enough. Unfortunately, we've sat through too many admissions committee meetings in which strong applicants have lost any chance of admission due to their interview. The message they sent during the interview was that they absolutely did not belong in this school. We believe that most of these applicants are completely unaware of the messages they send during the interview. Be it the inappropriate answers to interview questions, the mannerisms that overshadow the message, the affect that hides their true qualities, or the subtle findings that send a negative message, we believe that most of these applicants just didn't realize what messages they were actually sending.

Interviewing is not a skill where you can just wing it. Too many students are overly confident about their abilities to convey their individuality, their strengths, and their fit for the school in one thirty-minute interview session. Too often, applicants prepare minimally or not at all for interviews. Such overconfidence has the potential to inflict serious damage. To interview successfully, you must anticipate the questions that will be asked, prepare your responses, and deliver them confidently.

In preparing for interviews, practicing both alone and with others is a must. With adequate practice, you can become comfortable with the interview process. Practice improves self-confidence. It also helps pinpoint deficiencies in your interviewing skills. You may not recognize your own tendency to twirl your hair, but an interviewer will find it distracting. Nervous habits, distracting mannerisms, poor grammar, a blunted affect, or a tendency to speak too softly may all be features that you're not likely to recognize in yourself.

Rehearing your interview in front of a mirror may help you identify some problems. Note body language, as it sends a significant message. Do you smile? Do you keep your arms folded across your chest? Do you clench your hands tightly?

Practice with a friend. Have him ask you interview questions, and respond as you would if you were at a real interview. Consider videotaping your performance. Together, you can review the interview, critique your performance, and use this information to make improvements in your verbal and nonverbal impressions.

Tip # 7

Speaking too long is a turn-off for interviewers. Limit your answers to two minutes. Most applicants have no idea how long their responses last, and therefore you should time yourself during a practice session.

One of the most useful methods of preparation, and one of the most underutilized, is to ask your advisor if he or she would feel comfortable helping you prepare by participating in a mock interview. Many advisors have considerable experience helping applicants, and therefore have valuable insights.

Tip # 8

Finding the right person to conduct a mock interview is important. Although friends and family are options, they often don't have experience in this area. Health professions advisors are worth considering, and some pre-health offices may hold interview workshops. Professional mock interview services are also available.

The mock interview with your advisor can be designed to simulate the real interview. Ask your advisor to assume that he knows nothing about you but the information found on your CV and personal statement. After the mock interview, meet with your advisor to evaluate your performance. Ask for specific feedback on the following:

- Content of your responses
- Your body language
- Your poise and level of confidence
- Whether he would select you based upon your performance

This type of feedback is valuable, and should be utilized. Make any necessary adjustments prior to your first actual interview.

Tip # 9

Urge your mock interviewer to provide specific information. Which of your answers were compelling? Which require additional work? Did you have any nervous or distracting mannerisms? Were you using annoying words or phrases such as "like," "awesome," and "you know?"

Did you know...

"Ask your mock interviewer about your speaking volume. Is your volume sufficient to appear confident? In our experience, applicants are more likely to be 'quiet' rather than 'loud.' If you are too quiet to be heard, it will raise concerns. Among these concerns are the following:

Is this person strong enough for medical school?
Will patients, students, and physicians intimidate this person?
Is there something to hide?"

University of Mississippi School of Medicine[14]

Admissions Officers Speak...

"Practice expressing yourself verbally so that you can provide thorough, logical answers within a short time frame. Participate in a mock interview event, have a friend ask you questions and give you feedback, or use a web cam to record your own practice responses. This can be a helpful way to see how you might improve your interview performance."[15]

University of Arizona College of Medicine

"If you believe, or someone tells you, that you don't interview well, then try to improve your interviewing skills. Interviewers want to discover both what you know and how you think as well as how you handle yourself in a stressful situation. Mock interviews are sometimes helpful, but honest feedback from the mock interviewer is essential."[16]

University of Missouri School of Medicine

"All prospective students are urged to discuss the interview component of the selection process with their premedical advisors. Many undergraduate schools provide mock interviewing experiences which give prospective students insight into the interviewing process and may perhaps relieve some of the fear and anxiety that many individuals seem to experience on the interview day."[17]

University of Maryland School of Medicine

"Try a mock interview with your friends, and ask them to listen to see if you are too dependent on words such as: 'like,' 'you know,' or 'er..whatever.' If so, practice using more professional speech – your way of speaking may be really important to medical school interviewers."[18]

Dr. Jane Buder Shapiro and Dean Joseph Pieri
Case Western Reserve University

Rule # 32   **Travel is part of your preparation**

Plan to arrive early for your interview, ideally the day before the interview. Also plan on a dry run from your hotel to the admissions office.

How will you get to the interview? Will you walk, drive a car, take the bus, or ride the train? How long will it take? Have you considered the traffic? Where will you park?

Travel Tips

- Confirm the exact day, date, time, and location of the interview before you travel.

- Check the weather forecast and bring appropriate items (umbrella, hat, overcoat, boots, gloves, scarf).

- Check and double-check all travel arrangements (flight details, hotel stay, rental car reservation).

- Create a list of everything you need to bring well in advance of the interview and check each item off as it's packed.

- Bring an extra outfit with you, in case of food spills or stains.

- Your interview outfit and materials should always be carried with you onto the plane. When you're packing, make sure your carry-on meets the size limitations.

- If you're bringing liquids onto the plane, keep them in a separate bag.

- Arrive into town as early as possible on the day before a morning interview. If you're flying, avoid late-evening flights, which may be canceled or delayed.

- Schedule a wake-up call with the hotel. However, hotels have been known to miss these, so also bring your own alarm clock, or set your phone.

- Consider your commute time when deciding what time to leave for your interview. Plan for traffic delays.

References

[1]Gardiner H. New for aspiring doctors, the people skills test. *New York Times*. Available at:
http://www.nytimes.com/2011/07/11/health/policy/11docs.html?pagewanted=all&_r=0.
Accessed March 3, 2013.

[2]Elam C, Burke M, Wiggs J, Speck D. The medical school admission interview: perspectives on preparation. *NACADA* Journal 1998; 18 (2): 28-32.

[3]University of Washington School of Medicine. Available at:
http://www.uwmedicine.org/education/md-program/admissions/applicants/pages/interview.aspx. Accessed March 6, 2013.

[4]University of New Mexico School of Medicine. Available at:
http://hsc.unm.edu/som/admissions/docs/Applicant%20Admissions%20Assessment.pdf.
Accessed March 23, 2013.

[5]University of Alabama Birmingham School of Medicine. Available at:
https://www.uab.edu/medicine/home/education/prospective/min-require-consid/factors.
Accessed March 13, 2013.

[6]Davis P. Medical school interviews: pearls and pitfalls. Available at:
http://www.umc.edu/uploadedFiles/UMCedu/Content/Education/Schools/Medicine/Admissions/Medical%20School%20Interview%20Pearls%20and%20Pitfalls.pdf. Accessed March 4, 2013.

[7]Fatemi O. First aid for your medical school interviews. Available at:
http://www.cavalierdaily.com/article/2004/10/first-aid-for-your-medical-school-interviews/. Accessed February 22, 2013.

[8]Medical school interviews – common errors of applicants. Available at:
http://www.studentdoc.com/medical-applicant-mistakes-3.html. Accessed March 13, 2013.

[9]University of Chicago Health Professions Handbook, the Office of the Dean of Students in the College, and the Newsletter of the Central Association of Advisors for the Health Professions. Available at: http://web.jhu.edu/prepro/health/Applicants/interviewing.html. Accessed February 22, 2013.

[10]Amorosa J. How do I mentor medical students interested in radiology? *Acad Radiol* 2003; 10: 527-35.

[11]Ali F. School spotlight – Drexel University College of Medicine. *The Pitt Pulse*. Available at: http://thepittpulse.com/pdf/FebruaryFinal.pdf. Accessed March 14, 2013.

[12]University of North Carolina School of Medicine. Available at:
www.med.unc.edu/admit/. Accessed March 12, 2013.

[13]University of Maryland School of Medicine. Available at:
http://medschool.umaryland.edu/admissions/faq.asp#31. Accessed March 12, 2013.

[14]Davis P. Medical school interviews: pearls and pitfalls. Available at:
http://www.umc.edu/uploadedFiles/UMCedu/Content/Education/Schools/Medicine/Admissions/Medical%20School%20Interview%20Pearls%20and%20Pitfalls.pdf. Accessed March 4, 2013.

[15]University of Arizona College of Medicine. Available at:
http://medicine.arizona.edu/admissions/tucson/interview_process. Accessed March 13, 2013.

[16]University of Missouri School of Medicine. Available at:
http://medicine.missouri.edu/admissions/visiting.html. Accessed March 12, 2013.

[17]University of Maryland School of Medicine. Available at:
http://medschool.umaryland.edu/admissions/interview.asp. Accessed March 12, 2013.

[18]Case Western Reserve University School of Medicine. Available at:
http://www.cwru.edu/provost/ugstudies/AdviceMedFall05.pdf. Accessed March 13, 2013.

Chapter 7

The Interview Day

Rule # 33   **Your interview begins long before you meet your interviewer.**

"If my secretary says that someone was rude or inappropriate to her, they will not get in."[1]

>   Jennifer Welch
>   Director of Admissions
>   SUNY Upstate Medical University

Your interview doesn't start when you sit down with your interviewer. It begins as soon as you enter the premises. Many applicants mistakenly assume they only need to "be on" during the interview. In reality, everything you say or do on the day of the interview may be noted and duly reported.

It's not unheard of for admissions officers to ask their administrative staff for their opinions of the applicants. They may ask the staff member about a candidate's appearance or behavior. Staff members have commented on a host of negative behaviors. These range from the disinterested applicant leafing through the waiting room *Sports illustrated* instead of school information, to the applicant with the arrogant, unfriendly demeanor, to the pesky applicant asking inappropriate questions, especially when the staff member is clearly busy.

Tip # 10

Be on your utmost professional behavior, not just during the interview, but throughout the entire visit. Schools can gain much insight into your personal characteristics by observing your interactions with other applicants, program staff, and others. The best rule of thumb is to conduct yourself as if there are hidden cameras watching your every move.

Tip # 11

Ask the receptionist where you can place your excess belongings (coat, umbrella, bag, etc.). You don't want to walk into your interview bogged down with clutter.

Interviews may not start on time. Applicants may wait as long as an hour or two. Since many interviewers are practicing physicians, patient care related issues can arise at any point and require immediate tending. Candidates have been known to approach the receptionist impatiently or rudely, demanding to know the reason for the delay. How you handle a situation of this type is very telling.

Admissions Officers Speak...

"From the moment you arrive in the morning–and your interactions with other candidates throughout the interview process, with faculty members, students, tours, the types of questions you ask–the attitudes that you have will be observed and reflect on you, and I think sometimes people can make a mistake by feeling like they've had their two interviews for the day; they've had their student interview; perhaps, now they're on a tour, and then, sort of relax a little bit and inadvertently may say something that they wish they hadn't, or make some comments that retrospectively they wish that they hadn't.[2]

Darrell Waggonner, M.D.
Chairman of the Admissions Committee
Pritzker School of Medicine at the University of Chicago

Admissions Officers Speak...

"Important sentinel behaviors positive (e.g., politeness, altruism, helpfulness) and negative (e.g., condescension, arrogance, rudeness) may only manifest during applicant interactions with perceived subordinates (e.g., the appointment secretary)."[3]

Andrew Lee, M.D.
Chairman of the Department of Ophthalmology at The Methodist Hospital

----

"A person's behavior to the receptionist says something about the person and how they deal with people who have power and with [those] people who do not."[4]

Charles Bardes, M.D.
Associate Dean of Admissions
Weill Cornell Medical College[4]

"Another not as common but more detrimental mistake is a lack of professionalism and maturity. Students should treat everyone with kindness and respect and know that they are being observed."[5]

Christian Essman
Director of Admissions
Case Western Reserve University School of Medicine

"If my secretary says that someone was rude or inappropriate to her, they will not get in. If someone is like that with a student host – a student that is hosting them for the night so that they don't have to pay for the hotel -- if they are rude or inappropriate or disrespectful, they will not get in. I've even had it where local hotels have called to just let me know about so and so. They'll call and say, 'Jen, I know that they are interviewing with you, and this is the kind of experience we've had with him/her.' And I think that is important because you are putting on that suit and you are becoming this person, but I want to know the real you. So it's really important that you are 'on' at all times."[1]

Jennifer Welch
Director of Admissions
SUNY Upstate Medical University

Rule # 34	**Be compulsive about bringing everything that you need.**

Bring the following with you to the interview:

- Application (AMCAS, secondary)
- Copies of any published articles
- Correspondence between you and the school
- Driving directions to the school
- Campus map
- Phone number of the Admissions Office
- Notepad portfolio with pen
- Money
- Parking ticket
- Personal items (dental floss, mint, etc.)

While the school will have copies of your application, your individual interviewer may not. Be prepared with copies in case your interviewer asks for your CV or personal statement. A patient emergency may result in an interviewer substitution, and your documents will prove to be handy in such situations. Keep all items in your notepad portfolio.

Tip # 12

Writing down the name and contact information of each admissions member that provided you with assistance will allow you to easily write your thank-you notes.

Admissions Officers Speak...

"You do not need to bring anything," writes the University of Colorado School of Medicine. "However, if you choose to bring something that was not included in your AMCAS application you may do so. Examples would be research papers that have been published or an award you received recently. If you do bring something please bring two copies, one for each of your interviewers."[6]

Rule # 35   Arrive early for the interview.

Start your interview day by arriving early. Plan to reach the city on the day before the interview. Stay as close to the school as possible. If possible, make a trip to the school so that you know exactly how to get there. In the morning, plan to be at your destination an hour before the start time. This cushion of time is very helpful when you're faced with the unexpected, such as heavy traffic, an accident, or bad weather. Running in at the last minute can affect your interview performance, as many applicants have learned the hard way.

Entering the designated interview location more than fifteen minutes before the start time can be just as bad. Arriving too early can make you seem anxious, and you may interrupt the staff as they set up for the interview day. Get to the school an hour early, and then find a spot to relax until 15 minutes before your interview start time.

When you do enter the reception area, introduce yourself to the office staff. "Good morning. My name is _____ and I have an interview today."

Even with meticulous planning, you may be late due to unforeseen events. Arriving late is one of the reasons that schools cite for not accepting applicants. It is possible to recover from this situation, but only if handled with great poise. If you'll be late, call the school to apprise them of the situation. When speaking on the phone, remain polite, no matter how flustered you are. Once you've arrived, take the time to compose yourself before entering the room. Apologize and explain, at an appropriate time, what detained you. Never rush in complaining about what happened.

Tip # 13

If you're driving, determine in advance the route you'll take. Plan an alternate route in case of heavy traffic. If you're taking the train or bus, learn the schedule and the specific line you'll be riding. Always have a back-up plan. What will you do if service is interrupted?

Did you know...

"The second guideline is to seem to be low maintenance...In general, don't seem fussy at all. Don't fret if the coffee you're being offered isn't brewed quite right. Don't complain about how long you had to wait for the elevator. If you have to stay overnight for an out of town trip, don't complain about the accommodations or the transportation. You want to seem like the kind of person who is easy to get along with, and complaining will convey the opposite impression."[7]

Dr. Susan Krauss Whitbourn
University of Massachusetts Amherst

Rule # 36   **Take part in the entire interview day**

Interviews with admissions committee members are just one part of the interview visit day. "The interview day also includes a welcome and overview of TUSM with the admissions director, an information session with a representative from Student Financial Services, and a tour of the medical school and lunch with second year medical students," writes the Temple University School of Medicine.[8] It is important to participate in all scheduled sessions.

"It's important that you don't make the judgment that one portion of that interview day is more or less important than another portion," writes Joni Krapec, Director of Admissions at the Pritzker School of Medicine at the University of Chicago. "Don't be at the lunch with current students and think that it's okay that your boyfriend who traveled to the school with you can come in to lunch, or you would rather meet a friend that you have on campus for lunch..." And similarly too when we've had people on the tour who are not paying attention to the tour and who are instead checking their phones and doing different things, it just conveys that you're not very interested in the school."[9]

Rule # 37   Project self-confidence, not anxiety.

It's common and completely natural to be nervous. However, you don't want to convey the message that you're an anxious, distracted, unqualified applicant. Your message should be that you're an extremely well qualified applicant, and therefore you are calm and confident. The first and best way to conquer anxiety is thorough preparation. Learning about the interview process, anticipating questions, preparing responses, rehearsing with friends, and performing a mock interview with an advisor are all important parts of interview preparation.

Despite extensive preparation, anxiety can remain a significant problem for some applicants. We have a few additional suggestions for the days before an interview:

- Utilize stress reduction techniques. Many articles and books provide specifics on effective techniques utilized by actors, professional athletes, and public speakers. Such techniques include controlled breathing, progressive muscle relaxation, and visualization, among others.

- Channel your nervous energy into concrete, positive actions. One example would be focusing on action items for interview preparation: re-read the school information or practice responses for anticipated interview questions.

- Direct your nervous energy into action unrelated to interview preparation. Expend extra adrenaline by heading to the gym or going for a run.

- Look over your application to remind yourself of your accomplishments. The school would not be interviewing you if they weren't impressed with what you have to offer. You have a great deal to offer a medical school, and you should be specific when reminding yourself of what you can bring to a school.

Tip # 14

Although of course you'll be nervous, you don't want to convey the impression of an anxious, nervous applicant. Medical school is inherently stressful. As such, interviewers seek applicants who are able to think clearly in the most stressful of situations. Avoid comments that convey anxiety.

Rule # 38   **Shake hands properly.**

You'll have the opportunity to shake hands when you first meet the interviewer and again when you complete the interview. You must be ready for a handshake at these two points. Not all interviewers will offer to shake hands. In general, the interviewee should follow the lead of the interviewer. If she doesn't extend her hand, don't offer yours.

The initial handshake is an important component of a first impression. Be prepared to shake hands by keeping your right hand free at your side, as opposed to clutching your portfolio. If you suffer from hyperhidrosis and are prone to sweaty palms, be prepared to subtly wipe your palm. Your goal is to convey self-confidence, not anxiety. Shake hands using a firm grip, conveying an impression of confidence. Avoid a weak, limp, or crushing grip. As it can be difficult to evaluate the quality of your handshake, you may need to solicit input from friends or colleagues.

Did you know...

In the *Lancet* article, "Getting a grip on handshakes," Larkin reported the results of a study by Chaplin in which the handshake characteristics of men and women were evaluated. Larkin wrote that "a strong correlation was found between a firm handshake – as evidenced by strength, vigor, duration, completeness of grip, and eye contact – and a good first impression...Given the power of first impressions, the researchers advise that women as well as men 'try to make that first handshake a firm one.'"[10-11]

Admissions Officers Speak...

"Make sure that you practice having a good handshake. And the two that are kind of the most difficult to be on the receiving end of is kind of the cold, dead fish handshake where you get kind of this limp collection of fingers...And then the other is kind of the one that we call the queens' curtsy where somebody kind of gives you their fingertips...And it sounds silly to actually practice a good handshake, but you'd be amazed in terms of first impressions what a good strong handshake can do for you..."[9]

Joni Krapec
Director of Admissions
Pritzker School of Medicine at the University of Chicago

Rule # 39   **The first few minutes of an interview are critical.**

As soon as you walk into the room, your interviewer will be sizing you up. Initial impressions may even dictate the course of the interview. A favorable first impression may lead to a more relaxed interview.

Below are key guidelines to promoting a favorable impression within the first few minutes of an interview:

- Dress well and be impeccably groomed.
- Stand up and greet the interviewer with a firm handshake: Hello, Dr. Smith. I'm Evan Chen. It's a pleasure to meet you."
- Smile when meeting the interviewer
- Walk into the room with confidence
- Make eye contact
- Pronounce the interviewer's name early: It's nice to meet you, Dr. Torot.
- Make small talk easily

You must have a polished entrance, introduction, and opening. In your mock interviews, practice even this early stage of the interview.

Note that small talk is an area that often makes applicants uncomfortable. In one study, based on interviewee reports of medical school interviews, researchers found that 5% of questions asked were conversational or non-medical. The authors wrote that "these questions may be helpful in making the applicant comfortable or establishing rapport. It is interesting, though, that the applicants posted these questions as most interesting or difficult."[11]

Tip # 15

After you're invited into the interviewing room, don't sit down until the interviewer offers you a seat. It's considered bad manners to be seated before the interviewer invites you to do so, or does so herself.

Tip # 16

"How has your day with us been so far?" is commonly asked at the beginning of an interview. You can use this opportunity to say something positive about the school.

Tip # 17

After introductions have been made, most interviewers will engage in some small talk. You may be asked the following questions:

- How was your trip here?
- Did you have any problems finding our office?
- What's the weather like in ____?
- Have you ever been to our [city]?

In answering, avoid long statements. The interviewer doesn't want to hear about the "terrible traffic," how much you "hate the snow," or the problems you had finding their office. To start off on the right foot, answer these questions with brief, positive answers.

Admissions Officers Speak...

"We look for first impressions because it's important how well you'd respond when you're dealing with patients or their families. You have to earn the trust of your patients so they'll follow your instructions and advice, fill their prescriptions, take their medicine. The little things are important. You greet your interviewers with a firm handshake and establish good eye contact, so when you're talking with them you can relate. If you don't establish good eye contact you can't communicate."[12]

Tom South
Dean of Admissions at the University of Arkansas for the Medical Sciences

----

"Individuals who interview and judge others for a living often form very strong first impressions. Typically, those individuals are flexible and those impressions are changeable, but those first impressions are nevertheless important."[13]

Roy Ziegelstein, M.D.
Johns Hopkins University School of Medicine

Rule # 40   **Nonverbal communication is a potent part of your message.**

In all personal interactions, communication occurs in two fashions: verbal and nonverbal. So much focus is placed on <u>what</u> applicants should say during the interview that they often neglect to focus on <u>how</u> they say it.

Nonverbal communication can be as important, and in some cases more important, than verbal communication. Body language cues can overcome the content of your interview answers, especially if your body language conveys hesitation, uncertainty, or a lack of conviction.

The University of New Mexico School of Medicine reinforces this message: "Applicants should pay attention to body language and refrain from nervous habits. Many applicants with outstanding academic credentials and a wealth of clinical and volunteer activities fail to gain entrance to the School of Medicine due to poor interview and communication skills."[14]

Interviewers do analyze body language, although this is mostly done on a subconscious level. Any inconsistency between verbal and nonverbal communication may raise red flags. We've interviewed applicants who can't send a consistent message. While their self-proclaimed greatest strength is passion and dedication, they're slouched in the chair, leaning on the armrest, and looking a little bored. Others say the right things, but seem to lack sincerity. In response to a question on why the applicant is leaving an engineering job to begin medical school: "I found that my passion lay not in spending hours..., but in spending time in an outpatient setting speaking with patients." Although the content here is fine, the poor eye contact suggests insincerity.

Tip # 18

Are you aware of how you communicate nonverbally? Most applicants aren't. When preparing for an interview, applicants focus most of their attention on verbal communication. Much less emphasis is placed on nonverbal communication or body language. In fact, many applicants don't even think about nonverbal communication. However, it's estimated that 65 to 90% of every conversation is interpreted through body language.[14] There are many qualified applicants who interview poorly because their nonverbal language is not congruent with the content of their interview answers. Participating in a mock interview is one way of learning how well you communicate nonverbally.

It's difficult, and in some cases impossible, to evaluate your own body language. We've interviewed applicants who send strong, clear messages with their unconscious use of body language. The student who twirls her hair constantly. The applicant who rests his head on his hand during the interview. The other applicant who's slumped down in the chair. The student who can't seem to maintain eye contact, even when stating how much they love your school. The applicant who keeps smiling and laughing, even when discussing a sad patient case. The student who maintains such a blunted affect that it's difficult to tell if he's bored, tired, or just at baseline. You'd be surprised how often such cues can lead an interviewer to make snap judgments about a candidate's qualifications.

Your own evaluation of this type of communication should include a conscious awareness of several items. What are you doing with your hands? How is your posture? Are you maintaining eye contact? While you can perform a self-evaluation, mock interviews are critical in evaluating your nonverbal cues. Mock interviews can be staged with colleagues, advisors, or interview coaches, and feedback should cover your nonverbal communication skills. Mock interviews can be videotaped as well. Reviewing your performance can prove uncomfortable but enlightening.

Successful nonverbal communication includes adhering to the following rules:

- Stand and walk with erect posture and shoulders back.
- Shake hands firmly. Avoid a limp or crushing handshake.
- Your facial expressions should be relaxed. Avoid indicators of excessive anxiety, such as the furrowed brow or tense jaw.
- Maintain appropriate eye contact. Don't stare down your interviewer.
- Hand gestures should be appropriate, and not overdone.
- Avoid excess. While you should smile and nod occasionally, some applicants exhibit nervous laughter or excessive head bobbing.

Did you know...

Weiten, in his book *Psychology Applied to Modern Life: Adjustment in the 21st Century,* wrote (citing the work of Riggio) "it has been found that interviewees who emit positive nonverbal cues – leaning forward, smiling, and nodding - are rated higher than those who do not."[15]

Rule # 41   **Avoid non-verbal distracters.**

It's equally important to avoid nervous and distracting habits. We could list endless examples, but here are a few of the most common:

- Looking down or glancing away
- Tapping the foot or drumming fingers on desk or chair
- Fiddling with jewelry or other accessories
- Twirling the hair
- Glancing often at the watch

Tip # 19

Failure to maintain eye contact while speaking may suggest a lack of confidence or even dishonesty. However, avoid prolonged eye contact. An interview is not a staring contest.

Body language 101

What should I do with my hands?

Rest your hands in your lap. It's acceptable to clasp your hands together, but don't clasp them too tightly or make a fist. Avoid folding your arms across your chest. This can create an impression of rigidity, unapproachability, or even dishonesty. Do not cover your mouth or touch your face while you speak. Avoid touching your tie, tugging at your collar, or straightening your clothing. We also recommend that you not hold your pen in your hand. Many applicants end up fiddling or tapping with it.

How should I sit?

Posture can weigh heavily in how others perceive you. Maintain an alert, straight posture while you sit, stand, and walk. Leaning forward slightly demonstrates interest. Applicants who slouch can appear lazy, unmotivated, or disinterested.

What should I do with my feet?

Keep your feet flat on the floor. You may cross your legs at your ankles. Do not rest your ankle on your opposite knee.

Admissions Officers Speak...

"Be aware of your body language as it conveys a significant amount of information regarding your confidence and demeanor. While cultures may differ with respect to greeting others, a firm handshake will be anticipated in most cases. It is important to look at your interviewer when responding to questions. Sitting in a comfortable position also denotes a level of confidence when communicating with others."[16]

Norma Wagoner, Ph.D.
Former Dean of Students
University of Chicago Pritzker School of Medicine

"During the interview, the interviewer isn't only listening to what you are saying; they are also observing your body language. When people are 'themselves' – being honest about their goals, motivations, strengths, weaknesses, challenges and interests — their body language shows it."[17]

Andre Shaffer, 4th Year Medical Student at Weill Cornell Medical College
Member of Committee on Admissions

"Nonverbal communication important to the University of Mississippi School of Medicine includes timeliness, appearance, body language, voice and volume, energy level, eye contact, maturity, professionalism, and attitude."[18]

University of Mississippi School of Medicine

Avoid certain mannerisms, such as "excessive hand movement, staring at the ground while speaking, and loud laughing."[19]

John Zic, M.D.
Associate Dean of Admissions
Vanderbilt University School of Medicine

Rule # 42	You need to know how well you're doing in an interview. Pay close attention to the nonverbal cues of the interviewer.

The interviewer's body language may be your only clue as to how well you're doing. Most interviewers won't interrupt you to tell you that you're rambling. They won't share with you that your last response came across as very defensive. Better than words, their posture, movements, facial expressions and tone of voice can indicate their reactions. This type of indicator can be useful if you make it a point to notice these nonverbal cues.

As we've stated before, interviews are stressful, and many applicants focus all of their attention on preparing their next response. In response to the simple "Tell me a little bit about yourself," one applicant went off on a five-minute monologue. She didn't notice the obvious impatience of my colleague and myself because she wasn't paying any attention to us. The interview is bilateral communication, and it's very important to monitor how well you're doing. In many cases, your only effective way to do so is by paying close attention to the nonverbal cues of the interviewer.

Did you know...

"Nonverbal communication is a two-way street in an interview. You need to be able to communicate about yourself but also you need to read your interviewer's cues. If your interviewer seems bored, impatient, or annoyed, you need to figure out, quickly, where this is coming from. It might have nothing to do with you, in which case you have to work harder to get the interviewer's attention. But it might very well be you who is causing the boredom. Perhaps your answers are too long or too far off topic. Stop talking and wait for the next question."[7]

Dr. Susan Krauss Whitbourne
Professor
University of Massachusetts Amherst

Rule # 43   **The interviewer must sense that your focus is on her and not on your next response.**

We've sat in interviews where applicants were obviously nervous and distracted. They misunderstood the question or provided an answer that didn't address the question. Some asked questions that were answered earlier in the interview.

It's extremely stressful to be seated in front of an interviewer anticipating the next question. Many applicants are nervous, and are focused most on what they're going to say next. They should be focused on the interviewer instead.

Your goal is to create an impression of focus, interest, poise, and confidence. You are paying attention. This doesn't mean waiting for the chance to speak. It means concentrating on what the interviewer is saying, and making it clear that your entire attention is focused on the interviewer. I can picture these types of students. They're leaning forward slightly, they're maintaining eye contact, and they are clearly listening to what I have to say. That's a big difference from the applicant who is nervous, fidgeting, and who appears distracted.

Did you know...

"A Good Listener:

- Indicates listening by nodding and making acknowledging responses (e.g., "I see," "uh-uh").
- Avoids interruptions or distractions
- Asks open-ended questions that carry no pre-judgment
- Checks by paraphrasing or reframing, showing that he/she has heard accurately and fully
- Concentrates on what is being said rather than his/her own response"[20]

University of Washington School of Medicine

Did you know...

If you don't understand a question or comment, ask for clarification. Some interviewers may purposefully ask ambiguous questions to assess your response. You'll create a far better impression if you take the time to understand the question as opposed to blurting out the first thought that comes to mind.

Rule # 44   **Plan what you'll do when you don't know how to answer the question.**

One of an applicant's greatest fears going into an interview is that she'll be asked a question to which she does not know the answer. While preparation and practice are the best defenses against the unexpected, we do think that some reassurances and suggestions here are necessary. Remember that one subpar interview response is unlikely to torpedo the entire interview. Most important is that you maintain your confidence and focus.

If you're asked a difficult question or one that you're not sure how to answer, don't stammer, don't apologize, and don't make up an answer. Don't rush into a disjointed and hurried answer.

You do have several options in this situation. You can pause for a few seconds to gather your thoughts. You can also state "That's an interesting question. Let me think about it for a moment." If the question is ambiguous, you can also ask the interviewer for clarification. Remind yourself that with many questions, there are no simple right or wrong answers. If you still can't come up with anything other than "I don't know" or "I'm not sure how to answer that question," say so. Being able to say "I don't know" can take a great deal of confidence.

Above all, don't view one subpar interview response as the end of the world. In almost all cases, your recovery is likely much more important than your response to a single question. Maintain your composure and focus on the next question. If, at the end of the interview, you come up with an answer, then volunteer it. "I've been thinking about one of the questions you asked me earlier. Would you mind if I expand on my answer?"

Admissions Officers Speak...

"Some candidates begin answering the question the instant the last word rolls off of the interviewer's tongue. Some of these same students have not clearly thought out their answers, and ramble while they are getting their thoughts together. Finally, they decide how they feel about it, and answer the question directly after many unrelated sentences. I think this is because candidates feel that an awkward silence is uncomfortable and to be avoided at all cost…It is much better to pause for a second or two and gather your thoughts than to blurt out a stream-of-consciousness response that takes a circuitous route to the answer."[21]

Quinn Capers, M.D.
Associate Dean for Admissions at the Ohio State University College of Medicine

----

If you freeze on a question, "realize that this is ok and not that unusual. Instead of panicking, simply take a moment to think about your answer. It's perfectly ok to ask for clarification of the question if you didn't understand it. If you don't know that answer it's even ok to say, 'Hmmm, that's a great question. Let me think about that.'"[22]

MedPrep Program at Washington University

Rule # 45   **Learn how to handle silence.**

You should be prepared for silence during an interview, as it's not uncommon. Sometimes, inexperienced interviewers sometimes just can't come up with any more questions. Other times, silence is used as a deliberate tactic. Following your response, your interviewer may simply stare, without saying a word. The natural response, of course, is to wonder what you did wrong. "Did I just say something wildly inappropriate?" "Did she not like my answer?" Some applicants actually respond by rewording an answer, repeating a comment, or even retracting an answer.

While applicants often jump to the conclusion that the interviewer didn't agree with the answer, this tactic is often used to gauge an applicant's confidence in their response.

The best course of action is to simply remain silent without fidgeting or appearing anxious. Look at the interviewer with interest as you wait for the next question. Eventually, the interviewer will break the silence with the next question.

How can you tell if your interviewer is testing you or just can't come up with anything else to say? If her attention is focused on you, it's more likely that she's utilizing this stress tactic. If, on the other hand, the interviewer appears nervous, is fidgeting, and isn't looking at you, she may be trying to come up with the next question. In this case, you could break the silence by asking some questions about the medical school.

Rule # 46   **If the interviewer asks if you have any questions about the medical school, the correct answer is always "Yes."**

Most interviewers will set aside some time, usually at the end of the interview, for your questions. There are two main advantages to asking questions:

- You can gather information about the school in order to make an informed decision.
- You can demonstrate to the interviewer your interest in the school.

When the interviewer asks, "Do you have any questions about the medical school?" the right answer is "Yes, I do." One of the worst answers you can give is "No, I don't have any questions." This is akin to saying, "I have no interest in your medical school," which may or may not be true.

Tip # 20

When the interviewer asks "Do you have any questions?" this generally signifies the closing phase of the interview. If you didn't have the opportunity to communicate important points earlier, you can use the opportunity to do so. "Before I ask my first question, I'd like to take a moment to mention a few other points. Would you mind if I do so now?" Keep your comments concise, especially at the closing phase of the interview.

Applicants often come prepared with one or two questions, only to find that their questions have been answered during the course of the interview. When they're then asked about questions, they're forced to respond with the polite "No, I believe you've answered all my questions."

Prepare at least five questions in advance. A few cautions with these questions. Don't read them off a piece of paper. Never ask a question that's already been answered. This entails listening intently throughout the interview, which is a topic for another rule. Ask the right types of questions. We provide examples in the next rule.

Another note: even if all your questions were answered by a previous interviewer, there's no reason you can't utilize the same set of questions again.

Admissions Officers Speak...

"Have five (5) substantive questions about the school ready to go before the interview. Maybe they are from your research about the school, maybe they are from what you have observed so far during your time there, maybe they are questions about special interests you have for your medical education. Make sure the answers are not readily available to you from information sent to you, on the school's website or from the MSAR."[23]

Keith Bradley, M.D.
Program Director of Research Associates Program
St. Vincent's Hospital Medical Center

"What I hear from people is like, 'Oh no, all my questions have been answered.' And what goes through my mind is, I have no idea how many questions you asked, I don't know what those questions were, and I don't know what kind of information you wanted. And even though they may have been great questions and you've got great answers to them, I've now lost out on an ability to judge your thought process by you not asking those same great questions. So even if you don't have any new questions at that point, ask the same questions again."[2]

Darrel Waggoner, M.D.
Chairman of the Admissions Committee
University of Chicago Pritzker School of Medicine

"Ask questions during your interview and throughout your visit."[24]

Florida State University College of Medicine

Rule # 47	The questions that you ask an interviewer send a message. Don't ask the wrong questions.

Don't ask questions to which you should already know the answers. If the information is described in the school's brochure, the assumption is that you didn't bother to read the brochure, and that you're clearly not all that interested in the school. Therefore, the first rule of asking the right questions is to research the school before you arrive. Read the brochure. Read the school information that's sent before the interview. Study the school's website. Read the profiles of the faculty members.

Types of questions that may be perceived in a negative fashion:

- Don't get so personal that you make an interviewer uncomfortable. "Are you married?" "How many children do you have?"
- Don't suggest a bias. "Will I be working with a lot of HIV patients?"
- Don't exhibit a poor sense of taste or strange sense of humor.
- Don't ask questions that could be interpreted as aggressive. Be especially careful with "Why" questions. "Why doesn't the school have any exposure to transplantation medicine?"

Your goal is to ask intelligent, thoughtful, and specific questions. Too often, applicants ask general questions that could be asked of any school. Finally, ask your questions in an appropriate fashion. If you're not careful with your language usage or your tone of voice, your interviewers may feel that you are grilling, challenging, or confronting them.

Did you know…

"I would avoid asking any questions regarding the likelihood of your acceptance," writes the MedPrep Program at Washington University. "I would also avoid questions about the school or about medical school in general that you should already know such as, 'So what's the format of medical school? Are we in the classroom for two years and then the hospital?' Such a question would make you appear ill-informed about the general process of becoming a physician."[22]

Tip # 21

While you're free to ask general questions about the school, specific questions that demonstrate that you have researched the school will have more of an impact. A great resource to help you tailor your questions is "Thirty-five Questions I Wish I Had Asked" developed by the AAMC Organization of Student Representatives.[25]

Rule # 48   You may be asked inappropriate or illegal questions. Plan in advance how to handle them.

Results of the 1996 AAMC Medical Student Graduation Questionnaire revealed that 45% of students were asked about marital status or family plans during residency interviews.[26] Despite efforts to eradicate questionable interviewing practices, interviewers continue to ask applicants inappropriate, unethical, or outright illegal questions. Since some residency interviewers also serve on medical school admissions committees, it's not a stretch to believe that these questions may be asked of medical school applicants.

In fact, because of prior experiences, some medical schools actually address this issue on their websites. In an analysis of interviewee reports of their medical school interview experiences, researchers found that approximately 2% of questions asked were about marital status or family plans.[27]

Federal and state civil rights acts make it unlawful for employers to discriminate on the basis of:

- Religion
- Age
- Race
- Gender
- Sexual preference
- Marital status/living situation
- Family planning
- Height
- Weight
- Military discharge status

While questions that address these issues may be illegal or inappropriate, most aren't asked out of malice, but out of simple ignorance. Naïve or less experienced interviewers sometimes ask such questions simply to make conversation, not realizing how inappropriate these questions are.

Before you begin the interview process, develop an effective way to handle these types of questions. Some applicants, unprepared for such questions, have unfortunately reacted in an emotional manner. Some have refused to answer the question and some have even responded in a hostile manner: "This is a completely inappropriate question. I can't believe you would ask me that."

An outright refusal to answer an improper question is certainly your right. However, you'll offend the interviewer and create a situation from which you may not be able to recover. It goes without saying that if the question is blatantly offensive, then you should consider this option.

If at all possible, however, you should try to answer the question as you would any other, with poise and confidence. There are several possible strategies to utilize. We describe two ways of handling these types of questions.

Answer the question directly

Some applicants will simply answer the question directly. If you're comfortable answering the question, then this may be the right approach for you. If the interviewer has asked the question just to make conversation, it's unlikely that your response would affect your chances of acceptance. If the interviewer is deliberately asking the question, then your response may have a direct impact on your admission.

"I see that you're a nontraditional student, already in your 30s. When do you plan on having children?"

Examples of direct responses:

"My husband and I hope to have children in the next few years."

"My spouse and I have discussed it, and we'd like to delay until after medical school, since it would be so challenging during school."

"We really haven't come to any decision yet on that issue."

Answer the intent or concern behind the question

Using this approach, you won't directly answer the question. Your goal is to address the interviewer's concern. The key is to try to understand why the question is being asked.

"I see that you're a nontraditional student, already in your 30s. When do you plan on having children?"

This applicant assumes that the question is asked to determine if she would continue to be a focused, dedicated student in the event that she were to have a young child at home during her education and training.

"Dr. Lowell, I understand that the practice of medicine is demanding. I can assure you that I have a strong work ethic and sense of responsibility, and that my family responsibilities will not interfere with my ability to deal with a demanding patient case load in the future. You'll find that my transcript and letters of recommendation attest to that fact."

Did you know...

"It's possible you will be asked 'off the wall' questions you may deem improper or inappropriate, and which even may be illegal. For example, Pomona applicants have been asked about their marital status, sexual behavior, precautions used to guard against pregnancy, religious views, local baseball or football team preference, etc. Some of these may be legitimate questions badly phrased. Others are conspicuously improper.

You cannot predict such questions. But do contemplate how you would respond in a way that will not offend the interviewer and thus jeopardize your chances of being accepted. Try to rephrase the question into something that is acceptable. In other cases, you may wish to decline to answer. Don't become either antagonistic or angry.

If you believe that you have had a poor interview, or if you regard the behavior of the interviewer as less than professional, contact the medical school's Admissions Office immediately, since they may be able to arrange a new interview for you before you leave the school. We would also very much appreciate hearing about your experience."[28]

Pomona College

Did you know...

"If you feel you have been asked inappropriate or illegal questions, please contact the admissions office and/or an HSA staff advisor right away (i.e. before the end of the interview day) and explain the situation. If the admissions office concurs that you were asked illegal or inappropriate questions, they may schedule another interview while you are still there. Once an admissions decision has been made, it is too late to make any changes."[29]

University of California Davis

Rule # 49   **You need to make a good first impression. You also need to leave the interviewer with a good final lasting impression.**

Earlier we discussed the importance of making a good first impression. You also need to leave the interviewer with a good final lasting impression. You can do so by telling the interviewer you were glad to meet her. Thank her for this opportunity to meet, and for considering your application. Leave with a smile, direct eye contact, and a firm handshake if the interviewer extends her hand to you.

Some applicants go a step further by expressing interest in the school:

"Thank you very much for taking the time to interview me. I've really enjoyed my visit and have been quite impressed with your school. I would be very excited to be a student here. Is there any other information I can provide for you?"

Tip # 22

Practice your closing statement so that you can deliver it smoothly.

Tip # 23

Although you'll have your own thoughts about how the interview went, don't discuss or reveal these to your interviewer. We've seen candidates end their interviews, unfortunately, with sighs of relief or disappointment. Always end your interview in a confident, self-assured manner.

References

[1]2012 SUNY Upstate Admissions Q & A with Jennifer Welch. Available at: http://www.accepted.com/chat/transcripts/2011/med06062011_suny.aspx. Accessed March 12, 2013.

[2]University of Chicago Pritzker School of Medicine. Available at: http://pritzkerpodcast.com/2007/09/10/3-the-interview-day-mp3/#more-56. Accessed March 12, 2013.

[3]The Successful Match: Getting into Ophthalmology. Available at: http://studentdoctor.net/2009/08/the-successful-match-interview-with-dr-andrew-lee-ophthalmology/. Accessed April 1, 2013.

[4]Weill Cornell Medical College. Available at: http://www.theetiquettefactor.com/?page_id=14. Accessed March 13, 2013.

[5]Gibson P. Application secrets from a pro. Available at: http://tour4diversity.org/application-secrets-from-a-pro. Accessed March 21, 2013.

[6]University of Colorado School of Medicine. Available at: http://www.ucdenver.edu/academics/colleges/medicalschool/education/Admissions/apply/Pages/InterviewDayInformation.aspx. Accessed March 22, 2013.

[7]Whitbourn S. Selling it: making interviews work for you. Available at: http://www.psychologytoday.com/blog/fulfillment-any-age/201101/selling-it-making-interviews-work-you. Accessed March 22, 2013.

[8]Temple University School of Medicine. Available at: http://www.temple.edu/medicine/admissions/invited_for_interview.htm. Accessed April 12, 2013.

[9]University of Chicago Pritzker School of Medicine. Available at: http://pritzkerpodcast.com/2010/01/11/26-interview-tips-mp3/. Accessed March 15, 2013.

[10]Larkin M. Getting a grip on handshakes. *Lancet* 2000; 356: 227.

[11]Chaplin W, Phillips J, Brown J, Clanton N, Stein J. Handshaking, gender, personality, and first impressions. *Journal of Pers Soc Psychol* 2000; 79: 110-7.

[12]University of the Ozarks. UAMS dean of admissions demystifies medical school application process. Available at: http://alumni.ozarks.edu/news/news_story.asp?newsID=4495. Accessed March 13, 2013.

[13]The Successful Match: Interview with Dr. Roy Ziegelstein. Available at: http://studentdoctor.net/2009/06/the-successful-match-interview-with-dr-roy-ziegelstein/. Accessed March 13, 2013.

[14]University of New Mexico School of Medicine. Available at: http://hsc.unm.edu/som/admissions/docs/SelfAssessment.pdf. Accessed March 24, 2013.

[15]Weiten W, Lloyd M. *Psychology applied to modern life: adjustment in the 21st century.* Thomas Wadsworth 2005.

[16]Association of American Medical Colleges. Available at: https://www.aamc.org/students/aspiring/basics/284806/interview1.html. Accessed March 23, 2013.

[17]Shaffer A. What you need to know for a medical school interview. *The Cornell Daily Sun*. Available at: http://cornellsun.com/node/45764. Accessed March 23, 2013.

[18]Davis P. Medical school interviews: pearls and pitfalls. Available at: http://www.umc.edu/uploadedFiles/UMCedu/Content/Education/Schools/Medicine/Admissions/Medical%20School%20Interview%20Pearls%20and%20Pitfalls.pdf. Accessed March 4, 2013.

[19]Vanderbilt University School of Medicine. Available at: www.vanderbilt.edu/hpao/documents/Zic_9-18-07.ppt. Accessed March 28, 2013.

[20]University of Washington School of Medicine. Available at: http://www.uwmedicine.org/Education/MD-. Accessed March 22, 2013.

[21]Ohio State University College of Medicine. Available at: http://medicine.osu.edu/students/admissions/Documents/InterviewingTips.pdf. Accessed February 22, 2013.

[22]Washington University MedPrep Program. Available at: http://pages.wustl.edu/medprep/virtual-advisor/medical-school-interview. Accessed March 22, 2013.

[23]Bradley K. So...you have a medical school interview. Available at: http://www.raprogram.org/yahoo_site_admin/assets/docs/So_You_Have_a_Medical_School_Interview.349102805.pdf. Accessed March 4, 2013.

[24]Florida State University College of Medicine. Available at: http://med.fsu.edu/?page=mdAdmissions.interview. Accessed March 22, 2013.

[25]Association of American Medical Colleges. Selecting a Medical School: Thirty-five Questions I Wish I Had Asked. Available at: https://www.aamc.org/students/applying/programs/. Accessed March 22, 2013.

[26]1996 AAMC Medical Student Graduation Questionnaire. Available at: http://aamc.org. Accessed March 23, 2013.

[27]Rippentrop A, Wong M, Altmaier E. A content analysis of interviewee reports of medical school admissions interview. *Med Educ Online* 2003; 8.

[28]Pomona College. Available at: http://www.medsci.pomona.edu/interviewing.shtml. Accessed March 23, 2013.

[29]University of California Davis. Available at: http://advisingservices.ucdavis.edu/advising/hsa/handouts/medical_school_interview.html. Accessed March 22, 2013.

Chapter 8

Interviews: Common, But Not Always Obvious, Pitfalls

Rule # 50   Medical student interviewers wield significant power in the admissions process.

Medical students are members of admissions committees at many medical schools. In a survey of over 80 U.S. medical schools, 74% reported medical student involvement in the admissions committee. Medical student involvement is highly valued with 79% of respondents indicating that student contributions were "very important." Another 19% reported that the contributions were "somewhat important."[1]

As committee members, students may be involved in interviewing applicants. Research has demonstrated that the addition of medical student interviewers offers schools some advantages:

- Applicants share more information with medical student interviewers when compared to faculty interviewers.[2-4]

- Since medical students are closer to the "medical school experience" than faculty, students are better able to assess fit between the applicant and school.[5-6]

- Students have also indicated that they feel "particularly well placed to detect 'prepared' or insincere answers because they had themselves been through a similar process recently."[5]

One study compared interview score evaluations of applicants by faculty and medical student interviewers.[7] Both groups assessed such factors as motivation, personality, communication skills, medical experiences, and interests outside of the medical field. However, medical students wrote two or three times more words about motivation, personality, interests, and communication skills. Analysis of the overall evaluation section revealed similar results. Both groups were similar in their frequency of negative examples.

Medical Student Speaks...

"As an interviewer I run very laid back, get-to-know-you interviews. The person I'm interviewing has been deemed by powers higher than I to have the intellectual ability to function well and survive medical school, therefore my goal is to determine how they interact with people and how well they will fit in at our school. So, from the perspective of an interviewer, my advice is to do your best to be a normal human. Don't be cocky or rude or obscene, don't take over the interview and ask me questions before I clarify everything in your app I had questions about. Just sit up straight, look put-together, act professional and be yourself...as long as yourself isn't cocky, rude and obscene."[8]

Medical Student on the Admissions Committee at a Texas Medical School

---

Admissions Officers Speak...

"With the inclusion of medical students on its admissions committee, Indiana University School of Medicine joins the large majority of American medical schools that also include students on their admissions committees. The student members of the Admissions Committee at Indiana University School of Medicine are full participants in the admissions and candidate selection process, as well as full voting members on the admissions committee."[9]

Indiana University School of Medicine

Admissions Officers Speak...

"It's crucially important to have students involved in the admissions process. They understand what it's like to be a student here. They are living the life of a student and can fully appreciate the culture, the community and whether the applicant would actually be happy here."[10]

Richard Zeff, Ph.D.
Assistant Dean for Medical School Admissions
University of Connecticut School of Medicine

"We have [medical] students on the [admissions] committee, and they are often more critical of certain aspects of the applicant. There are times when the applicant gets high marks at a faculty interview, but a student says the applicant is disrespectful. Just be yourself, but recognize that you are interviewing for a professional school."[11]

Kim Bader, M.D.
Keck School of Medicine Admissions Committee Chair

"There are two components: a student interviewer and a faculty interviewer. Initially, a current medical student first year through fourth year will have lunch with the interviewee. They'll ask questions and see if they are a good fit for our school and whether or not they are genuinely interested."[12]

Lisa Cifelli
Director of Admissions at Drexel University College of Medicine

Rule # 51   **Don't become so focused on your next answer, or your fatigue, or your anxiety, that you fail to convey your deep enthusiasm for the practice of medicine and this medical school.**

"When I reviewed the interview performance of over 200 students who applied to our training program in the last 5 years, the single biggest reason for a low interview score was 'did not appear interested, no spark.'"[13]

> Patrick Duff, M.D.
> Associate Dean for Student Affairs
> University of Florida College of Medicine

It doesn't matter how well you've prepared the content of your interview answers. The manner in which that content is conveyed has a great deal to do with its reception. Your goal is to appear personable, sincere, and down-to-earth. We've seen many applicants who unfortunately appear tired, flat, or robotic. This can happen easily over the course of a long interview day: it's easy to stiffen up, become too formal, or become so focused on what you're going to say that you fail to convey a personality. In all of these cases, you may fail to connect with your interviewer. Worse, you may leave a frankly negative impression.

Admissions Officers Speak...

"People in medicine are driven. They embark on a difficult path that requires a great deal of study, hard work and sacrifice because they are inspired. This quality is intrinsic, not extrinsic — and it is something that is absolutely necessary (but not sufficient) to be successful in medicine. To that end, interviewers are going to ask you questions that aim to elucidate what's driving you. One of the things that determines whether you gain admission is how dynamic you are in describing your passions, activities and interests..."[14]

Andre Shaffer
4th Year Medical Student at Weill Cornell Medical College
Member of Committee on Admissions

"As stated earlier, if you are invited for an interview, that medical school has decided that you probably have the goods to succeed at their institution. So, be excited! You are on the cusp of something great and your dreams are within reach. Leave your interviewer with the impression that you are happy to be there and grateful for the opportunity. Even if it is your last-choice medical school, approach the interview with gratitude and humility, and imagine yourself walking those very same halls as a medical student. Because, well, you just might."[15]

Quinn Capers, M.D.
Associate Dean for Admissions at Ohio State University

Rule # 52   **Don't complain about the small stuff.**

Interviewer: Welcome to Baylor. How was your flight to Houston?

Interviewee: It was the worst flight. It was cancelled and I had to scramble and catch another flight, then I had to connect through Oklahoma City. By the time I got in last night, it was midnight.

In response to innocently asked questions at the beginning of an interview, I've had applicants complain about their flight, their hotel stay, the directions to the school, the weather, and even the parking.

Many schools caution their students about complaints, precisely because this is such a common pitfall. Admissions interviewers hear these over and over, and this negativity, not surprisingly when you think about it, leaves a negative impression.

Rule # 53   **Don't complain about the big stuff.**

Interviewer: What did you find to be the most challenging aspect of your undergraduate experience?

Interviewee: The most difficult part was my thesis advisor. He...

While all of this may be completely accurate, this is neither the time nor the place to discuss it. Your goal in an interview is to keep the focus on your motivations and your accomplishments, and ultimately how these will benefit the medical school. The Career Development Office at Smith College counsels their students: "Never be led into a situation where you criticize the college, another institution, or a person. The assumption is that if you are unhappy in one place, you might be unhappy in another. If asked about situations that were less than ideal, emphasize the learning or growth you gained from the challenging experience."[16]

Rule # 54   **Avoid phrases that suggest a lack of credibility.**

Schools are on guard against applicants who exaggerate their achievements or outright lie. Therefore, you need to safeguard your own credibility. Avoid the following phrases:

- I'm going to be honest with you now...
- To tell you the truth...
- To be perfectly candid...

Prefacing a statement with phrases such as these may raise a red flag in the interviewer's eyes. She may assume that what you're about to say will be a stretch of the truth or a flat out lie. The reason we specify these phrases is that many individuals who use them are unaware of their use, and are unaware of their connotations.

Admissions Officers Speak...

"Honesty and integrity are essential in both the medical education process and eventual practice of medicine. Applicants should be able to articulate an understanding of the importance of ethical behavior, of honesty, of professionalism in medicine. Dishonesty on the application form or in the interview as well as information provided in the letters of evaluation will be considered in assessing integrity."[17]

University of Michigan Medical School

Rule # 55   **Don't ever be remembered for what you're wearing.**

I've interviewed a few applicants who were distinctly memorable. I can still, to this day, remember exactly what they were wearing. I can't remember what their scores or strengths were, but I can remember the dangling, hypnotic earrings, the too-short skirt with the high heels, and so many more. In an interview, you never want to be remembered for what you were wearing. You want to be remembered for your strengths, your communication skills, your great scores, and your outstanding letters of recommendation--or any or all of these.

You should dress conservatively, and your goal should be to appear neat and professional. In choosing interview attire, select clothing in which you feel comfortable. Your clothing should not interfere with your ability to give a successful interview.

Interview Attire		
	Yes	**No**
Men	Suit, well-fitting, dark blue, gray, or black Shirt, ironed, long-sleeved, typically white Tie, long, conservative Belt color that matches shoes Shoes, clean, polished Matching socks up to mid-calf Well-groomed hairstyle (neat and trimmed beard and mustache) Nails, clean, trimmed	Earrings Flashy cuff links, rings, or chains Visible body piercings Strongly scented cologne Strongly scented aftershave
Women	Pant or skirt suit (dark blue, black, brown or gray), or tailored dress Blouse, solid color with collar Shoes – clean, closed toe, dark or neutral color, low to moderate heels Hosiery, conservative, at or near skin color Well-groomed hairstyle Nails, clean, trimmed (if nail polish, clear or conservative color)	Low neckline Excessive or distracting jewelry Strongly scented perfume Distracting hair or make-up

Your appearance is of the utmost importance, since it's one of the first factors that telegraphs a message during an interview. If you're sloppily dressed or poorly groomed, your message is that you are not the highly professional, mature physician with compulsive attention to detail that the medical school seeks.

Admissions Officers Speak...

"[Before coming to an interview], cover up your tattoos; take out your piercings. You don't know who you are going to be getting at the interview. Dress for success not for failure."[11]

Ellena Peterson, Ph.D.
Associate Dean of Admissions
University of California Irvine School of Medicine

"Pitfalls include casual clothing, extremely high-heeled shoes, shirt collar too tight, and skirt too short."[18]

Stephen Case, Ph.D.
Associate Dean of Admissions
University of Mississippi School of Medicine

"It is perfectly acceptable for women to wear pants suits, but if a skirt is chosen, it should not be so short that when in a seated position, it rides up to an uncomfortable level. Tugging on a too-short skirt throughout the interview is distracting and will definitely be noted by the interviewer...Please note that some schools provide a walking campus tour during the interview day. For women applicants from a warm climate, coming to Chicago in the middle of winter, remember that sling back high heels won't work. Once you know the school's schedule, prepare for clothing needs throughout the day."[19]

Norma Wagoner, Ph.D.
Former Dean of Students
University of Chicago Pritzker School of Medicine

"Applicant should dress in formal business attire: suits and ties for the men and suits for the women. Women may wear pant suits or skirt suits (skirts should not be short). Applicants should dress as conservatively as possible and avoid excessive jewelry."[20]

Herbert Wertheim College of Medicine at Florida International University

----

"Most applicants wear formal business attire to their interview. We encourage you to wear shoes that you feel comfortable walking in and that have closed toes, as we will be visiting clinical sites on the tour. During our colder months, we also encourage you to watch the weather reports and be sure to pack warm clothing."[21]

University of Vermont College of Medicine

Rule # 56   **In the olden days, it was "please refrain from smoking." Now, it's "please turn off your cell phone."**

In recent years, I've repeatedly heard stories from admissions officers about inappropriate cell phone etiquette during the interview visit. One applicant even answered the phone during the interview and proceeded to speak. Interviewers also disapprove of applicants who are gabbing, texting furiously, or surfing the internet while waiting for the interview.

When asked about the common mistakes students make during the interview day, Christian Essman, Director of Admissions at Case Western Reserve University School of Medicine, had this to say: "Another not as common but more detrimental mistake is a lack of professionalism and maturity. Students should treat everyone with kindness and respect and know that they are being observed. Don't be asleep or on the phone texting/facebooking. My advice is to turn your cell phone off during interview day. We can all go 6 hours without our phone. If there is a family emergency where you might be on your phone, let someone in the admissions office know."[22]

Cell Phone Etiquette Tips for the Interview Day

- Turn your cell phone off before you enter the school's admissions office.

- If you must turn it on during the interview day, it is essential that you turn it off before walking into the interviewer's office.

- Placing your phone on vibrate mode is not acceptable because the buzzing sound that comes with a new e-mail or phone call could affect your conversation with the interviewer.

- If you feel the need to take down a few notes during the interview, do not use the cell phone for this purpose. Be sure to bring a notepad portfolio.

Rule # 57   Clean up your online persona.

Letters of recommendation. Transcript. AMCAS application. Your social media presence. All are important components of the med school application.

Social media presence? Some medical schools and residency programs are now assessing an applicant's social media presence, and possibly using the information in the selection process. Researchers at the Miller School of Medicine at the University of Miami, led by Dr. Carl Schulman, surveyed 600 medical school admissions officers and residency program directors. Nine percent reported using social networking websites in the selection process. The study was published in the Postgraduate Medical Journal.[23]

"There is no question in my mind that some percentage of medical admissions officers and residency directors do go online and Google and Facebook people to see what they've got up on their personal sites," said Dr. Henry Sondheimer in a Kaiser Health News article.[24] Dr Sondheimer is the Senior Director of Medical Education projects at the Association of American Medical Colleges (AAMC).

In 2008, we raised this as a potential issue in an article written for the Student Doctor Network, and offered advice to applicants on how to manage their online presence.[25]

Did you know...

"I suggest students begin by doing a search of their own name. It is important to do this through the 'Image' search as well, to see what is out there. I suggest they remove photos where they are less than 70% dressed. I also suggest they look at the background of their pictures for anything inappropriate, as the actions of their friends could be a reflection on them. I suggest they do not post status updates about sensitive issues such as politics or religion. Finally, I suggest they speak to their friends about not 'tagging' them in any photos that are not appropriate."

Brian Clinton
Biological Sciences Advisor
University of Rhode Island

Rule # 58   **There are always two major goals of all interviews. Don't forget the second one.**

You must have a clear understanding of your goals for the interview. All of your goals can be summed by the major two:

1. You must have a successful interview in order to gain admission.
2. You must gather enough information about the school to make an informed decision about accepting an admissions offer in the event that you're offered acceptance to multiple schools.

In your desire to demonstrate your perfect fit with the school, you may lose sight of the second goal. While it may not always feel that way, remember that the interview process involves two parties selling themselves. While the school is trying to ascertain your strengths and weaknesses, you should be doing the same with respect to the school. You must use the short time that you have during your visit to learn as much as possible about the school. With every school you visit, ask yourself the following questions:

- How compatible am I with this school?
- Can I see myself working well with the school's faculty and students?
- Will this school provide me with an environment in which I can thrive?
- How well will this school help me meet my future goals?

Admissions Officers Speak...

"The interview is, and should be, a two way street. The interview provides each applicant an excellent opportunity to visit our campus, view the basic science and clinical facilities, meet our faculty, staff and students and have questions answered by individuals knowledgeable about the medical school and its educational, research and community missions. Our interviewers expect applicants to ask them questions and are prepared to answer those questions to the best of their abilities."[26]

University of Maryland School of Medicine

"Keep in mind that you are sizing up the school as much as they are assessing you."[27]

David Trabilsy
Former Assistant Dean of Admissions
Johns Hopkins University School of Medicine

References

[1]Arnold D, Coe R, Pepper M. Structure and function of medical school admissions committees. *J Med Educ* 1984; 59: 131-2.

[2]Salvatori P. Reliability and validity of admissions tools used to select students for the health professions. *Adv Health Sci Educ Theory Pract* 2001; 6: 159-75.

[3]Eva K, Reiter H, Rosenfeld J, Norman G. The ability of the multiple mini-interview to predict preclerkship performance in medical school. *Acad Med* 2004; 79: S40-2.

[4]Gelmann E, Steward J. Faculty and students as admissions interviewers: results of a questionnaire given to applicants. *J Med Educ* 1975; 50: 626-8.

[5]Koc T, Katona C, Rees P. Contribution of medical students to admission interviews. *J Med Educ* 2008; 42: 315-21.

[6]Roby L. The medical student interviewer. *J Med Educ* 2008; 42: 746-8.

[7]Gutowski C, Thaker N, Heinrich G, Fadem B. Current medical student interviewers add data to the evaluation of medical school applicants. *Med Educ Online* 2010; 15.

[8]Mind on Medicine Blog. Available at: http://mindonmed.com/2011/09/interviewing-for-medical-school.html. Accessed March 22, 2013.

[9]Indiana University School of Medicine. Available at: http://www.iupui.edu/~mscstaff/?q=node/60. Accessed March 23, 2013.

[10]University of Connecticut School of Medicine. Available at: http://today.uconn.edu/blog/2012/08/medical-student-volunteers-offer-vital-role-in-admissions-process/. Accessed March 22, 2013.

[11]Keck School of Medicine at USC. Available at: http://trojanhealthconnection.com/?p=117. Accessed March 12, 2013.

[12]Ali F. School spotlight – Drexel University College of Medicine. *The Pitt Pulse*. Available at: http://thepittpulse.com/pdf/FebruaryFinal.pdf. Accessed March 14, 2013.

[13]2012 SUNY Upstate Admissions Q & A with Jennifer Welch. Available at: http://www.accepted.com/chat/transcripts/2011/med06062011_suny.aspx. Accessed March 12, 2013.

[14]University of Florida School of Medicine. Available at: www.med.ufl.edu/oea/osa/student_advice.shtml. Accessed March 12, 2013.

[15]Ohio State University College of Medicine. Available at: http://medicine.osu.edu/students/admissions/Documents/InterviewingTips.pdf. Accessed February 22, 2013.

[16]Smith College. Available at: http://www.smith.edu/lazaruscenter/pdf/med-school.pdf. Accessed March 12, 2013.

[17]University of Michigan Medical School. Available at: http://med.umich.edu/medschool/admissions/apply/Admissions-Policies-Procedures.pdf. Accessed March 12, 2013.

[18]University of Mississippi School of Medicine. Available at: http://msuamsa.blogspot.com/2011/08/minutes-from-august-25th.html. Accessed March 13, 2013.

[19]Association of American Medical Colleges. Available at: https://www.aamc.org/students/aspiring/basics/284824/interview10.html. Accessed March 15, 2013.

[20]Herbert Wertheim College of Medicine at Florida International University. Available at: http://medicine.fiu.edu/admissions/md/interview/index.html. Accessed March 12, 2013.

[21]University of Vermont College of Medicine. Available at: http://www.uvm.edu/medicine/admissions/?Page=interviewFAQ.html#wear. Accessed March 23, 2013.

[22]Application secrets from a pro. Available at: http://tour4diversity.org/application-secrets-from-a-pro/. Accessed April 8, 2013.

[23]Schulman C, Kuchkarian F, Withum K, Boecker F, Graygo J. Influence of social networking websites on medical school and residency selection process. *Postgrad Med J* 2013; 89 (1049): 126-30.

[24]Tran A. Medical schools may check applicants on facebook. *Kaiser Health News.* Available at: http://capsules.kaiserhealthnews.org/index.php/2012/11/status-update-medical-schools-may-check-applicants-on-facebook/. Accessed April 2, 2013.

[25]The Successful Match: Facebook, a new way to screen applicants. Available at: http://studentdoctor.net/2008/11/the-successful-match-social-networking-sites-a-new-way-to-screen-residency-applicants/. Accessed March 23, 2013.

[26]University of Maryland School of Medicine. Available at: http://medschool.umaryland.edu/admissions/interview.asp. Accessed March 23, 2013.

[27]Reflections of a Former Admissions Dean. Available at: web.jhu.edu/prepro/Forms/Trabilsy.Admissions.Dean.doc. Accessed February 22, 2013.

Chapter 9

Interview Questions

How are you today?

Did you have any trouble getting here?
How do you like the weather?
It's quite a cold/hot/snowy/rainy/windy day, isn't it?
Did you have any trouble finding a place to park?
How do you like [our city]? Have you ever visited before?
Was there a lot of traffic on your way here from the airport (or hotel)?
How do you like living in _____?
I see that you go to [school/university]. How do you like it?
What do you prefer to be called?
How has your visit with us been so far?

The above questions, known as icebreaker or "small talk" questions, are usually asked at the beginning of an interview. While this portion of the interview may only last several minutes, its importance can't be overemphasized. If you answer these questions well, you can set a positive tone for the rest of the interview, and put both you and the interviewer at ease.

Tip # 24

Small talk sets the tone for the conversation that follows. Think about how you would answer the above questions positively.

These questions appear simple and straightforward. Many applicants we've interviewed, though, handle them poorly. Generally, applicants prepare well for the deeper questions, but give no thought to these types of icebreaker questions. Savvy interviewers recognize this and purposefully engage applicants in small talk. In doing so, they hope to learn more about an applicant's true personality.

The key with this type of interaction is to reinforce your overall message. It's therefore important to respond in a confident and positive manner. In response to "how are you today?" an answer such as "I'm doing great. I'm really happy to be here today" conveys much more enthusiasm and energy than "OK" or "tired." Unfortunately, we've all interviewed applicants who end up whining or complaining about one thing or another. You may hate the weather or the traffic. You may have had difficulty finding the office or struggled with the commute. There's no reason to share this with the interviewer.

Tip # 25

Be careful in how you respond to questions about your arrival. Remember that the school has provided you with directions and may have helped you with other travel arrangements.

Tell me about yourself

What brings you here?
Tell me about why you are here.

This question is typically asked at the start of an interview. It's often the first question asked, or the first question following icebreaker questions. Given its common use, you should prepare for this question in advance. Script and rehearse your response.

In developing your response, include the type of information that the medical school wants to know about you. What is impressive about your qualities or achievements? What sets you apart from other candidates? Why should the school select you?

Too often, applicants give their entire life stories, beginning with when and where they were born. Don't interpret this question as one that's focused purely on your personal background. Rather, regard it as an opportunity to share your most important skills, experiences, and accomplishments. In developing your response, focus on what qualifies you to be a medical student at their school.

Tip # 26

Never assume that the interviewer has read your application. Many don't. That's why it's important to share key aspects of your background and credentials in your answer. Interviewers often base their next question on the information you convey in your response. By highlighting certain aspects of your background, you make it easier for the interviewer to ask questions on the topics you wish to discuss.

Think of your response as a positioning statement. The questions that the interviewer asks next will often be based on the information you provide.

Summarize your background in no more than two minutes. Time yourself to make sure you don't exceed this time limit. Avoid providing irrelevant details, since we can state from personal experience that many candidates tend to ramble needlessly.

Because this question can be interpreted in different ways, interviewers are also eager to learn about your approach. What do you focus on? How do you organize the information? Your content and delivery provides the interviewer information about your composure and communication skills.

Sample answer (Margot)

"My interest in medicine began during college. At the end of my freshman year, my grandmother was diagnosed with dementia, and I decided to take a year off to tend to her needs. As her primary caregiver, I was responsible for taking her to all of her doctors' visits. In doing so, I was able to see firsthand the interactions between my grandmother and her physicians. I was really struck by their bedside manner, the way in which they comforted her, and their efforts to provide compassionate care. Although there was no cure for her dementia, it was comforting for our entire family to have a dedicated group of physicians involved in her health.

After returning to college for my sophomore year, I decided to explore medicine further. By shadowing physicians, working as a certified nurse's aide, and performing medical research, I feel that I've gained a better understanding of the roles and responsibilities of physicians. I know that the road to becoming a physician is long and challenging, but I can't think of anything that I would rather do.

In college, what I've found most satisfying are the times when I've been able to help others in some way, whether it's through mentoring middle-school children, or launching a new fundraising drive to benefit our school's free health clinic. I've also been involved in student government, and this year I'm serving as Vice-President. This opportunity has helped me build my leadership skills, and I know that will help me in my future. I'm excited about a career as a physician, and thrilled to be here today. I've heard many wonderful things about the school from friends who are medical students here. Thank you so much for inviting me for an interview."

Why do you want to be a doctor?

What led you to pursue a career in medicine?
What stimulated your interest in medicine?
Name a meaningful experience you've had and how it's shaped you to pursue work as a physician.
What major influences in your life led to your decision to pursue medicine?

In the box below, we've listed typical answers to this very important question. What crucial piece of information is missing?

Answers to the Question "Why do you want to be a doctor?"

"It's been in the back of my mind for some time. I don't think there was a single thing that made me say that this is what I want to do. With my parents both being physicians, I think being around it so much, having a chance to work in a lab and actually do research, and, in school, taking different kinds of science classes. So, in a way, it now feels like I can't imagine that I ever thought that I could do anything else. If you asked me two years ago, I wouldn't have said that. At that point, I was thinking go to grad school and do something in physics or chemistry. Then I realized that I wanted to do something where I could not only do research but also be involved in the practical application of research."

"It was a gradual process. When I first started at MIT, I took an EMT class they had there and became a certified EMT. In doing that, I learned a lot about medicine. But I also wanted to focus on my engineering. But in the last couple of years was when I really made my decision to go into med school and not engineering. I realized that I am so much more fascinated with medicine than anything else and wanting to make a career out of that."

In neither response do you see any mention of the applicant's desire to help people. This is a damaging omission, and happens more often than you would think. As an admissions committee member, I can't tell you how many times I've heard interviewers speak glowingly about an applicant's credentials and background, only to be disappointed by the interview. In many cases, this is due to the applicant leaving out any mention of his or her desire to help people. In other cases, applicants don't appear sincere: they may offer trite expressions, such as "I really want to give back", but lack any evidence to support their assertion. Rule #7 describes the results of research that evaluated different motivations for a career in medicine. The views of admissions officers regarding these different factors are included.

At the beginning of this chapter, you read how Margot answered the question, "Tell me about yourself." Below is her response to the question "Why do you want to be a doctor?"

Sample answer

"I would say that my path to medicine really started while working as a certified nurse's aide. I was able to care for people at difficult times in their lives. From bathing to shaving to feeding, I've been involved with patients in many capacities. No matter what I was doing I tried to connect with patients, listen to their stories, and maybe bring out a smile. Being able to provide emotional and social support was very satisfying. During that time, I decided to further explore the medical profession through shadowing. I marveled at how doctors started with a patient's symptom, and pieced together information from the history and exam to reach a diagnosis. Discussing the science behind the medical problems was fascinating, and reminded me how much I've enjoyed my science courses, especially anatomy and biochemistry. What also struck me was the bedside manner, the way these doctors comforted patients in times of distress or uncertainty. I remember one patient who came in with fatigue and poor work performance. He told me that he was nearly fired and would have been had the doctor not diagnosed him with sleep apnea. After receiving treatment, he felt like a new man, and had even received an award at work. Seeing this, it became clear that medicine was exactly what I wanted to do."

Why our school?

What qualities are you looking for in a school?
Describe your ideal medical school.
What interests you most about our school?
Tell me what you know about our school.
Why do you want to be a student here?
What two or three things are important to you in a medical school?

A strong response to this group of questions was reviewed in the introduction to the book. We've repeated it here for ease of use.

While the question asks about the school, the best answers highlight the applicant. You need to make a strong case that YOU are the perfect fit for this exact school. Few applicants are able to do that well.

Here are examples of the typical responses that I've heard over the years:

"Well, I've lived here for three years so I know that I would want to live here. One of the things I like is the diversity and clinical opportunities you offer. I know I would see all kinds of different patient populations. The school has a good reputation which I know would help me getting into a good residency program. The atmosphere is excellent, students help each other, and this is a place which will challenge me but not bring out the worst in me."

"I'm really looking for two things. First, a program that really integrates the clinical with the basic sciences. My impression is that Baylor does a good job with that. The second thing is the breadth of opportunities here. All the research that's going on. I can't imagine that it would be difficult to find many people I would be interested in working with."

"It seems like the school will help you reach your goals. You also have a lot of hospitals you can work at. Also, I'm interested in the International Health Track."

"The shorter basic science period really appeals to me. The way the basic science is structured: for example, the way anatomy is spread over a number of semesters. I really like the medical center and Houston. The center is top notch."

What do all of these responses have in common? They're all underwhelming. While there a number of reasons for this, the main one is that all of these applicants end up sounding pretty generic. The responses are fine and nobody's sending up any red flags, but at the same time, you'd be hard pressed to remember any of these applicants.

Why is that? First, most of these responses are too brief. Second, most of these responses lack specific details about the school, and all of them lack specific details about the applicant. Third, there's very little here that would convince the interviewer that this specific applicant would be a perfect fit with the school. And finally, there's nothing memorable in any of these responses. In other words, just about any applicant could have given the same response.

The biggest fail here is that every single applicant lost out on a valuable opportunity to impress the interviewer.

To see how a student could answer this question in a more compelling manner, let's meet Elena, an undergraduate student in Arkansas.

Elena's story

Elena grew up in a medically underserved area with a significant Latino population. There were relatively few primary care physicians in her community, and even fewer specialists. Several of Elena's relatives passed away of cancer, and Elena has developed an early interest in oncology. After finishing medical school, Elena hopes to pursue residency training in internal medicine followed by fellowship training in oncology. She plans to return to her hometown to practice oncology, and would be one of only two oncologists serving a four-county area. In college, Elena worked with Dr. Garcia, a dermatology faculty member at a local area medical school, to develop an instructional module to help primary care physicians differentiate benign from cancerous skin lesions. The main goal was to provide a resource for primary care physicians practicing in parts of the state lacking access to dermatologists. Elena was also involved in organizing and implementing skin cancer screenings in these underserved areas.

Elena's answer

"I first heard about your school from my faculty mentor, Dr. Garcia. Your school has an excellent reputation, and she spoke very highly of the education you offer. You're also well known for quality of teaching and diversity of patients, which I value. I also would love to live in Dallas, and have family in the Fort Worth area."

Analyzing Elena's answer

Be as specific as possible to confirm that your selection of their school was based on some thought and effort. Too often, applicants give a general answer. If you could give the exact same answer at another school, then your answer isn't good enough. If you examine Elena's response, you'll see that her answer, for the most part, was short on specifics. A better response is shown below.

Begin by researching the school thoroughly. What makes this school unique? What aspects of the school or its curriculum do you find particularly compelling? This information allows you to tailor your responses. In simple terms, if the school highly values research, and you have an interest or experience in that area, then you need to discuss it.

If a faculty member recommended the program, then by all means say so, as Elena did. Schools like to know that they're well regarded. Speaking with someone who has firsthand knowledge of the school also demonstrates that you've taken the time and initiative to learn as much as you can about the school. It demonstrates the seriousness of your interest.

There are also certain responses that you need to avoid at all costs. Avoid answers that confirm a disconnect between what you're seeking and what the school offers. Never put down another school. Lastly, while the geographic location of the school may be a major factor in your interest, avoid offering school location as the only or initial reason for applying to the school.

A better answer

"I first learned about your school through my faculty mentor. Dr. Garcia is a graduate of your school and she's always spoken highly of the training she received. I would love to be a medical student at your school for a number of reasons. In shadowing physicians, I've learned that it's important to go to a school that places an emphasis on clinical skills. Your school has a reputation for being a leader in clinical skills development. The early patient contact, frequent observation of skills followed by regular feedback, and simulation lab are particularly appealing to me. It's also important to me that I develop a strong foundation for the practice of high quality care with patient safety in mind. That's why I'm really excited about your unique patient safety curriculum. And finally, I know that your school has a track for the underserved, and I could really see myself thriving in this track. In college, some of my most rewarding experiences occurred when I was involved in organizing and implementing health fairs for rural communities. Receiving education in caring for the underserved population would be fantastic because I would like to make this an important part of my future career in medicine. I grew up in a medically underserved area, and would like to return to my hometown as an internist and oncologist. On a personal note, I do have family in the Fort Worth area, and training in Dallas would allow me to spend time with family."

Tip # 27

Many applicants do an excellent job researching a school in advance. Unfortunately, many don't know how to, or don't feel comfortable with, demonstrating this knowledge. Some end up making no reference at all to the specific information that they've read or learned about the school. Others end up asking the type of basic questions that could have been asked by any other applicant. The end result is a generic interview, and a lost opportunity to demonstrate your strong interest in the school.

To help develop your own answer highlighting your fit with the school, begin with a list of your own experiences, accomplishments, and qualities. Then review Rule #5, which highlights the qualities that medical schools seek. The rule also includes the results of a survey about the personal characteristics that are important to medical schools and are therefore assessed during the interview. Rule #10 provides some further information on fit with a school, while Rule #15 describes how to research an individual school. Rule #16 reviews a related subject, that of how to research the type of student that the school seeks.

What are your weaknesses?
What is your weakness that concerns you the most?
What about yourself would you change if you could?
What are your shortcomings?

This is a difficult question, because it forces you to say something negative about yourself. To answer it best, prepare by asking yourself some questions. What are your weaknesses? What have you done to improve? What are you doing now about them? What effects have your efforts had on your weaknesses?

Let's meet John, a student majoring in biology at a large university in Florida.

John's story

John was elected president of his school's premedical AMSA chapter, and spearheaded a "Dangers of Smoking" campaign targeting middle school children. His plan was to develop an interactive PowerPoint presentation to educate students on the dangers of smoking, solicit the participation of 40 students to visit the local area middle schools, and train the volunteers to deliver these presentations. The project was large in scope, and, although the AMSA chapter was one of the larger student groups on campus, John had difficulty delegating the work involved to other student members. As the deadline for the project approached, John worked night and day to complete the tasks while trying to keep up with his course load. The project was a success, and his chapter received a commendation from AMSA.

John's answer

"One thing I'm trying to improve is that sometimes I'm a bit hard on myself when things don't go as planned. Sometimes I tend to take on too much."

Analyzing John's answer

The worst answer you could possibly give is saying that you have no weaknesses. Everyone has weaknesses, and saying that you have none will prompt the interviewer to assume that either you think too highly of yourself or that you lack self-awareness. Thankfully, John has offered a weakness. Since some interviewers ask for several, you should prepare three weaknesses to discuss. Do not, however, offer more than what's requested.

You are not obliged to share your worst qualities with the interviewer. Unfortunately, many applicants do just that, sometimes because they're taken off guard. When choosing a weakness to discuss, avoid including one that is damaging. If your weakness would interfere with your ability to function as a medical student and physician, then present a different one. Stating that you're often late or have trouble working with other people would be highlighting damaging weaknesses. Avoid sharing a character flaw or a negative personality trait. These can be difficult, if not impossible, to change. A poor answer to this question can easily remove your application from further consideration.

Classically, applicants have been advised to relate a potential strength as a weakness. One example of this approach is the classic "People tell me I'm a workaholic." Who wouldn't want a student with a strong work ethic? Equally common is the "perfectionist" example. Who wouldn't want a student who pays close attention to detail? "I expect too much of others" is another commonly used example. This suggests that you set high standards. Yet another example is "I try to be friends with everyone." This suggests that you would be a good team player. We caution you on these four examples. Because many applicants have used these weaknesses over the years, they have become trite and unoriginal, and interviewers are tired of hearing them.

John chose to speak about "being hard on himself when things don't go as planned." In the medical profession, "things" don't often go as planned, and this requires practitioners to be adaptable and resilient. In offering this response, the interviewer will be looking for evidence that indicates that John is taking steps to improve in this area. Unfortunately, John hasn't offered this support. You must always end your response with the steps you've taken to correct your weakness.

A better answer

"When I began my term as our AMSA chapter President, my ability to delegate tasks and duties were not as good as they could have been. I approached faculty leaders at my school to see how I could improve my delegation skills. Listening to their stories and recommendations helped me a great deal. I also attended a five-day leadership program developed by AMSA and the George Washington University School of Medicine. Through this program, I learned how to delegate, manage, and motivate large teams. My efforts have helped me become a better leader, and our AMSA chapter has been able to make meaningful contributions to our school and community."

Do you have any questions for me?

What questions do you have about our school?

Interviewers often leave some time at the end of an interview for applicants to ask questions. "What questions do you have for me?" is your signal that the interviewer is ready to answer questions.

Note that not all interviewers provide this opportunity. Some of my colleagues would rather not answer questions, and therefore never invite questions from applicants. If the interviewer is short on time, he may ask his last question and then proceed to close the interview. "It was a pleasure to meet you. I wish you the best of luck" is a clear signal that the interview is done. If you're not invited to ask questions, then don't.

It can easy for applicants to underestimate the importance of this question, because it can seem like just a polite gesture on the interviewer's part. However, it's an important opportunity to advance your agenda. You need to learn more about the school, and you need to emphasize your fit with the school.

Sample dialogue

Interviewer: Now that I've learned more about you, I'll be happy to answer any questions you might have. Do you have any questions for me?

Josie: "Ummm…No, all my questions have been answered. Thanks."

Analyzing Josie's answer

This is the worst possible answer. Many interviewers consider it a red flag when an applicant has no questions. The worst thing you can say is "No, I don't have any questions" or "My questions have already been answered." This can be interpreted as "I have no interest in this school." Your interviewer may also wonder if you've actually prepared for the interview. You also lose the opportunity to gain valuable knowledge about the school.

What questions should you ask? Too often, applicants ask standard or basic questions that have been answered at the school's website or in their brochure. Such questions imply poor preparation. [Didn't she bother to read the brochure?]

Your questions should convey the fact that you were interested enough in the school to research it in advance. To ask the "right" questions, begin by researching the school in great depth. Learn all that you can by using a variety of sources – the school's website, an internet search, the school brochure, your advisors and faculty, and current medical students. Savvy applicants begin their question with a reference to what they've learned (see below).

Often the best questions are those derived from a comment made earlier by the interviewer. "You mentioned that the school offers a unique lecture series to train students as researchers. What topics are covered in this series?"

Some other tips:

- After making a list of questions, prioritize them. You usually won't have the chance to ask all of your questions. If you could only ask a single question, which one would it be?
- Use your best judgment regarding the number of questions to ask and when to ask them.
- Ask open-ended rather than yes/no questions.
- Keep the questions short.
- Avoid "Why" questions. These can sound critical. [Such as: Why doesn't the school offer electives in the third year?]
- Be aware of the manner in which you ask your questions. If you're not careful with language and tone, your interviewer may feel that you are grilling, challenging, or confronting her.
- Take care in how you phrase a question. Avoid asking questions that suggest biases, such as "Will I have to work with a lot of HIV patients?"
- Do not interrupt. Always allow the interviewer to finish before replying.

A better answer

"On your website I learned that the school has a unique program: Developing Students into Teachers. I was excited to read about this because I've really enjoyed my teaching experiences as a tutor and teaching assistant. I understand that teaching workshops are offered through this program. Can you tell me more about these workshops?"

In this example, the applicant starts by making a reference to the school's website. She then proceeds to ask a thoughtful and specific question tailored to the school. In doing so, she clearly conveys her teaching experiences as a college student, her passion for this area, and her desire to continue it as a medical student. Since the school has decided that it's important to train students to become teachers, this applicant has succeeded in matching her interest and skills to the needs of the school.

FURTHER QUESTIONS

In this next section, we provide examples of other questions that interviewers may utilize. We've grouped together similar questions, and for each group we've highlighted the rules that will help you develop your own unique, strong responses.

What are your strengths?

What are your positive qualities?
Do you like to work alone or with other people?
If your best friends were asked to describe you, what would they say?
Describe your personality.
How would you describe yourself?
What would your best friend say about you in convincing me I should admit you to our medical school?
Describe yourself in three words.
What do you think are the most important qualities a person must have to be a good doctor? How do you rate yourself in these areas?

Interviewers want to know if you possess the attributes that are needed to make a great physician. Rule #5 describes the qualities that medical schools seek, and provides a list of personal characteristics that are important to schools, based on the results of research. One point I emphasize strongly here is that it's never enough to say "I'm a very hard worker." The best answers provide evidence to support your claims. Describe your strengths, and then provide examples or stories to back them up. The first section of this chapter provides strong examples of the use of evidence to strengthen a response. John, in the earlier example, would have plenty of evidence to support his assertion. "I'm a very hard worker. When I was president of our local AMSA chapter, I initiated a 'Dangers of Smoking' program. It took months of preparation, and required that I…"

What type of doctor would you like to be?

What specialty interests you?
What are your specific goals in medicine?
Where do you see yourself in 15 years?
Where do you plan to practice after you graduate?

Answering this question well involves reviewing your professional goals, and linking those to your past experiences. Do you envision a future as a clinician-educator? What types of work or volunteer experiences have prepared you for a career in academic medicine? Are you interested in a career as a physician-scientist? What is the depth of your research experience? Are you committed to serving an underserved population? How have you demonstrated that commitment thus far? You may or may not have any idea of what specialty you'll choose, but in gaining exposure to the world of medicine, you'll have observed or worked with physicians in different specialties. Which of those fields drew you in, and why?

No faculty member expects you to be absolutely certain of a specific path, but the best applicants have worked hard to obtain a working knowledge of what a physician's career entails. The best answers here highlight your work and volunteer experience, or your experiences in medicine, or your accomplishments, or any combination thereof. Even better answers highlight your fit with this school.

"There are many fields that I'm excited about exploring in medical school, and I plan to ultimately remain actively involved in teaching. My work in curriculum development at Striker and my volunteer work cemented that interest. That's one of the reasons I'm excited to be interviewing at Strong Medical - I've talked to several students about your workshops and electives in that area. Ultimately, my plan is to be a clinician-educator. "

How have you contributed to your community?

Many interviewers feel strongly that a future physician should have a demonstrated commitment to service. See Rule # 9.

How have you explored medicine as a career?

Is medicine a rewarding career? Why?

What health care experience have you had?

What clinical/hospital experiences have you had?

If you want to help people, why not social work?

Do you know what a real doctor's life is like?

What experiences have you had in the community that demonstrate a commitment to medicine?

What steps have you taken to acquaint yourself with what a physician does?

It's very important to interviewers that you've investigated the field of medicine, and that you know before you ever get to medical school what the medical profession entails. Rule # 8 reviews the importance of direct exposure to medicine. Also note that these questions are a great opportunity to discuss and emphasize your motivation for a medical career. Rule # 7 reviews research that describes the different motivations students have for a medical career, as well as how these motivations are looked on by admissions officers.

Tell me about your research experience

What extracurricular activities have you been involved in?

What leadership positions have you held?

Tell me specifically what you do in [activity].

What is your greatest accomplishment?

What have you done that shows initiative?

What are you most proud of about yourself?

I call these "opportunities to brag." These are the best kind of questions, because they're an invitation to highlight your accomplishments. They're also ideal opportunities to highlight your fit with the specific medical school. This can be difficult to do. You want to highlight your accomplishments without coming across as arrogant or conceited. Elena, in the earlier example, provided a strong example of how an applicant can do this well. She discussed her experiences, and linked her answer to her overall goals.

"What are you most proud of about yourself?"

"Some of my most rewarding experiences occurred when I was involved in organizing and implementing health fairs for rural communities. My colleagues and I had to overcome a number of challenges to complete these, including financial and logistical challenges, and I was proud that we were able to overcome these obstacles and accomplish what we had set out to do. These experiences reinforced my desire to work with underserved rural populations when I complete my training."

To prepare for this type of question, you need to review every single experience, activity, and accomplishment that's listed on your application. An interviewer may choose to ask you in-depth questions about anything that you've included on your application. Note that if you have significant research experience, you'll probably be asked about it. Make sure you review all your prior research experience, especially research that may have been done several years ago [Rule # 29].

Explain why your grade point average is lower than what we expect for applicants.

Why is your MCAT lower than what we expect for applicants?

If there are any red flags in your application, there's a strong chance that you'll be asked to address them. Rule # 30 reviews the approach for addressing weaknesses or deficiencies in your application.

Why should we choose you?

There are so many qualified applicants. Why should we pick you?
What do you have to offer our school?
What contributions can you make to our school?
What do you have to offer that others don't?
What will you contribute to the profession?

The strongest answer to this type of question incorporates elements of several preceding questions. What are your strengths? How are you a good fit for this medical school? What type of doctor will you be? What are you most proud of about yourself? Review your responses to these questions, and incorporate your prior experiences and accomplishments to back up your assertions.

What are some of the challenges facing medicine today?

What do you think about the changes that are taking place in medicine?
What do you think is the most pressing issue in medicine today?
What do you think about our healthcare system and the way it should go?
What do you think is wrong with the current healthcare system?
What problems do you see in health care now and in the next ten years?
What would you do to remedy health care in the United States?
Why do you think many physicians are unhappy practicing medicine?

Interviewers don't expect you to be a health policy expert, but you do have to demonstrate a working knowledge of the challenges facing healthcare today, as well as demonstrate an understanding of some of the expected changes. This includes the ethical implications of advances in healthcare, as well as the financial aspects of delivering healthcare in America. Useful resources to help you become more informed include the journal *Virtual Mentor*, which can be accessed online at the American Medical Association website. The *Health Care Handbook*, written by Elisabeth Askin and Nathan Moore, provides a great overview of current challenges and controversies in health care.

I don't know much about your [undergraduate university]. Can you tell me more about the school, and why you chose to go there?

How did you like your [undergraduate university]?
If you could change one thing about your [undergraduate university], what would it be?
Which of your college courses interested you the most?
What was your favorite course in college?
What was your least favorite course in college?
What was your most difficult subject in college?

As with several other categories of questions, these are often used to learn more about your qualities and interests. Specifically, does this applicant demonstrate the qualities that are required of a physician? [Rule #5]

On the other hand, some interviewers just want to hear you speak about a subject that interests you. They want to learn more about you, and will use this opportunity to evaluate your communication skills [Rules # 27 and 40], as well as your energy and enthusiasm [Rule # 51].

What was the last book you read?

What do you think about [current event]?
Tell me about a book that you read recently. Why does it interest you?
Tell me about a movie that you recently saw.
If you could be any character in history, who would it be? Why?
Who is your hero? Why?
Of all the people, dead or alive, who would you most like to have dinner with and why?
What are you passionate about?
What things give you the greatest satisfaction in your life?

These types of questions can be used to judge your communication skills. In addition, most interviewers seek applicants who have interests outside of medicine, which many believe makes for better physicians and provides important buffers for stress.

Can you converse easily and make eye contact appropriately? What are your interests outside of medicine [as in, do you have any]? These are also great opportunities to convey your energy and sense of enthusiasm. [see Rule # 51].

What causes the most stress in your life?

What things frustrate you the most? How do you usually cope with them?
Medical school is demanding and stressful. How do you normally handle and relieve stress?
Tell me about your study habits.
What scares you the most about medical school?
What do you think you will struggle with during medical school?

Medical school is extremely stressful, and it's very important to faculty that they choose applicants with a high level of personal maturity and established coping skills [Rule # 11].

Tell me about a time when you experienced a conflict with a colleague.

Tell me about a time when you successfully handled another person when that person didn't personally like you.

What has been the highest pressure situation you've been under in recent years? How did you cope with it?

Can you tell me about a significant challenge you had to overcome? How did you handle it?

Rule # 21 reviews the behavioral interview. This is a particular type of interview format, utilized because of the belief that past behavior predicts future behavior. With these types of questions, it's important to review your past experiences, and consider how these reflect your qualities. You may find it helpful to review the characteristics that medical schools seek [Rule # 5], as well as the rules related to personal maturity, integrity, and professionalism. [Rules # 11-13].

Chapter 10

After the Interview

Rule # 59   **Grade yourself after every interview.**

Some candidates leave an interview thinking they "aced it" while others feel like they "blew it." These opinions are usually based on the interviewer's disposition and bearing during the interview. Interviewers won't usually share their thoughts about your performance, and many hide their reactions well. Therefore, this type of thinking isn't productive. There are many students admitted to schools despite a supposed "bad" interview. There are many examples of the opposite as well: applicants who were sure they aced an interview, but never received an offer.

Since many applicants have more than one interview, it's more productive to ask the following questions after every interview:

- Did I make a good first impression?

- Did I answer each question appropriately and effectively? Was my answer concise?

- Were my answers supported by evidence whenever possible?

- Did any of the questions surprise me? Which ones? Why did they surprise me?

- Was I able to establish rapport with the interviewer?

- Did I make a good final impression?

- How can I use this experience to better prepare for my next interview?

Rule # 60   It's important to communicate with the school after the interview.

Is there a chance that your communication with a medical school after the interview will influence your chances of acceptance? In most cases, the answer is no. However, it is possible that your communication may have an effect on some interviewers.

Even if it has no effect on your chances of admission, it's considered common courtesy to express your appreciation. A small gesture on your part now may help you in the future. If you do matriculate at the school, you may find yourself working closely with the faculty interviewer.

Admissions Officers Speak...

"Say thanks. Email your interviewers and thank them for taking the time to talk to you. In all honesty, they've likely already evaluated you and this won't have any bearing on your likelihood of acceptance, but it's common courtesy. Interviewing and evaluating applicants is a time-consuming, mentally taxing process, so make sure your interviewer knows you appreciate their taking time out from a busy schedule to talk to you."[1]

Medical Student Member of the Admissions Committee in Texas

"Send a thank you note to your interviewers."[2]

University of Michigan Medical School

"Always send a thank you note to your interviewer (hand written are best) and get the person's name, title, and address before you leave. Mention something discussed in the interview if you can. Mailing a thank you before you return will ensure that it arrives promptly."[3]

Polly Allen, M.Ed.
Program Director
University of Vermont Postbaccalaureate Premedical Program

"Thank you notes are appreciated, but do not help or hurt your application."[4]

University of Washington School of Medicine

Rule # 61	The thank you letter serves as a chance to emphasize your overall message, so don't send a generic note. Send a compelling and memorable thank you.

The most effective thank you letters contain the following information:

- Statement of appreciation for the opportunity to interview and for the interviewer's time

- Expression of appreciation for information shared with you

- Expression of interest and enthusiasm for a position in the entering class

- Highlight your ability to make a contribution to the school by including a brief statement of why you are a good fit for the school

- Personalize the note by including a reference to a point raised or topic discussed during the interview

- Final statement of thanks

It's particularly important to emphasize how your qualities, skills, or strengths match the school's needs. What did you learn about the school that can help you explain more effectively why you are a good fit for the school?

Sample thank you notes may be found on our website:

www.TheSuccessfulMatch.com

Rule # 62   **Thank you letters may be sent in the form of a handwritten note, a typed letter, or an e-mail.**

All forms of thank you correspondence are acceptable. While individual faculty members may have their own preference, it would be impossible for you to know that preference. The handwritten note implies a great deal of time and care in its production, and immediately sends a more personal message. However, the production of multiple handwritten notes is difficult, especially if you follow the norms of sending one to every single interviewer, and include sufficient information to personalize the note. While the typed letter can easily be expanded to include more information, it can give an impression of mass production, and therefore may not be as memorable. You can, however, include sufficient detail to create a memorable letter and overcome this negative. The e-mail thank you may be seen as too informal and suggestive of a shortcut, particularly for more traditional faculty, but has the benefit of speed.

Our suggestion is to immediately send an e-mail thank you letter to every interviewer, preferably within one or two days. This should be followed by either a typed letter or handwritten note. Either type should include specific details that refer back to the interview, and should include specific information that substantiates your fit for the school.

Note that these are not necessarily the norms of post-interview correspondence. Hardly any students send immediate thank you e-mails, and few of the thank you letters we receive include the type of specific details that we suggest. Therefore, your utilization of these suggestions will aid in your goal of creating a memorable impression.

References

[1]Mind on Medicine Blog. Available at: http://mindonmed.com/2011/09/interviewing-for-medical-school.html. Accessed March 22, 2013.

[2]University of Michigan Medical School. Available at: http://www.med.umich.edu/medschool/interview/info.html. Accessed March 12, 2013.

[3]University of Vermont Postbaccalaureate Premedical Program. Available at: http://learn.uvm.edu/wordpress_3_4b/wp-content/uploads/PBPM-Newsletter-1-13-12.pdf. Accessed March 3, 2013.

[4]University of Washington School of Medicine. Available at: http://www.uwmedicine.org/education/md-program/admissions/pages/frequentlyaskedquestions.aspx#interview. Accessed March 3, 2013.

Chapter 11

The Wait List

Rule # 63   **The wait list represents a valuable opportunity.**

The wait list is a big mystery to most applicants. Does it mean that you've failed? Do you still have a chance? Is there anything you can do at this point, or is it all over?

The definitive answer to that last question is that it's <u>not</u> over. A spot on a wait list represents an important opportunity, and if you want to take full advantage of that opportunity, then it means more work. At some schools, you can actively impact your chances of admission, even at this late stage.

Start with the statistics. What are the chances that you'll be accepted off the wait list?

The proportion of the class that's filled from the alternate list varies from school to school. Some fill a high percentage of their class with wait list applicants, while others don't need to. Although often asked, schools don't provide firm answers on this subject, mainly because there are so many unknowns in the process and the percentage may vary widely from year to year. The Tufts University School of Medicine writes that "In some years, we have filled as many as a third of the seats in the entering class from the wait list; in other years, as few as a dozen."[1]

Admissions Officers Speak...

"This number varies from year to year and depends upon the decisions of the initially accepted applicants. As we receive withdraw requests from accepted students, we look to our alternates to fill the class. Some years we only accept 8 or 10 alternates. Other years we have accepted 30 from the alternate group."[2]

Emory University School of Medicine

"The greatest factor affecting your chances is the number of withdrawals we will receive before our class matriculates at the end of August. Any number of individuals currently holding positions in our entering class may also be holding multiple wait list positions at other schools, and any number of those individuals may receive an offer from another school and withdraw from Tufts to accept it. We simply do not know how many withdrawals we will receive between now and matriculation, and hence we cannot give you any meaningful assessment of the likelihood of your admission to Tufts. The number of applicants admitted from the wait list varies greatly from year to year. There is no meaningful average. In some years, we have filled as many as a third of the seats in the entering class from the wait list; in other years, as few as a dozen."[1]

Tufts University School of Medicine

Rule # 64   A wait list may be ranked or unranked.

This is probably the most important rule in this chapter. Read over this rule again, and think about the implications.

Many applicants assume that when the selection committee meets, they take all 600 applicants that they've interviewed, and then proceed to rank them. They offer spots to the first 200, and as they hear back from students, they move down the list.

This is the process at some schools - and it's hard to say which schools, because many don't release details about their selection process - but published information indicates that it's not true at all schools.

The University of Virginia School of Medicine provides some specifics about their wait list. "When positions become available in the class, the Alternate List will be reviewed much like a separate, self-contained admissions process. Several factors are involved in this process, including the in-state/out-of-state ratio in the class at the time positions become available. The Admissions Committee will select individuals from the Alternate List who are considered to be the most qualified at that point in time. Each time a position becomes available, this process will be repeated."[3]

If a school ranks their alternate list, you'll be given a number. You generally won't know this number, although some schools may provide a general estimate. As spots are declined by other applicants, the school will move down their rank list.

At schools with an unranked list, the applicants are placed in a pool, and it's up to the committee to choose from this group.

Rule # 65	**If a school has an unranked wait list, and is open to communication, then you can influence your chances of admission, even at this late stage.**

Many schools are open to communication and updates from applicants. If so, you have a chance, even at this late stage, to influence your chances for admission. At the George Washington University School of Medicine: "There is no traditional 1, 2, 3... ranking system and as such, we are unable to give you any indication as to where you stand with the committee. The wait list is very fluid so we strongly recommend sending in update letters and letters of interest throughout the year."[4]

While we'll provide more specifics about how to communicate with the admissions office, we'll also provide one overriding caution. If the school prohibits communication, then please follow their directions. If you fail to follow instructions, you can sink your chances of admission.

Tip # 27

Apprise the admissions committee of updates periodically, but don't overdo it. All committees have stories of pesky applicants who contacted the office every other day to the point of annoyance. "Don't badger the office with status calls," writes Sunny Gibson, Director of the Office of Minority and Cultural Affairs at the Northwestern University Feinberg School of Medicine.[5]

Admissions Officers Speak...

Among the pet-peeves were "overly persistent individuals, who frequently email, call, or write to the admissions office. Excessiveness indicates a lack of patience and an abundance of self-importance."[6]

David Trabilsy
Former Assistant Dean of Admissions
Johns Hopkins University School of Medicine

While you obviously don't want to be obnoxious or a pest about it, many schools do welcome updates about your progress and accomplishments. At the Creighton University School of Medicine,

"The Office of Medical Admissions advises candidates on the alternate list to inform the committee of updates (particularly grade reports), and any new information will be evaluated with your current application. Relevant information includes any new shadowing experiences, volunteer experiences, additional coursework, research or publications, awards, as well as anything else that the admissions committee has not seen. In short, advise the admissions committee on anything relevant that you have done since completing your initial application."[7]

When communicating in response to a wait list notification, begin by thanking the school and enthusiastically reiterating your interest. You may also offer any updates that make you a stronger candidate.

Have you maintained a 4.0 since the time of your application? Were you elected to a leadership position? Have you started a new shadowing or volunteer experience? Are you the recent recipient of an award? Did your research get published? Did you receive a promotion? Do you have a new letter of recommendation? All are examples of information that can be provided to the school in the form of an update.

What's the best way to communicate new information? We recommend either a letter or an email. You may also ask the admissions office what type of communication they prefer. When received, this letter or email can be added to your file. A phone conversation is less easily documented by extremely busy admissions offices.

While periodic updates and additional information may help at some schools, at others they won't influence your chances at all.

At other schools, while additional accomplishments may not make a difference, a clear indication that you're still available to join the entering class may help. This can be in the form of a letter or email stating that you remain very interested in attending this school.

The different viewpoints expressed by admissions officers are presented in the next section.

Admissions Officers Speak...

"Letting us know that you remain interested and available is most helpful, especially after July 1…We are happy to include in your file any new material you would like to send, such as spring semester transcripts or new letters of recommendation. However, it is not necessary for you to do this, and at this point in the process such material is unlikely to change the outcome of your application."[1]

Tufts University School of Medicine

"Because Alternate List applications are reviewed again when positions become available, you are welcome to add materials to your file at any time. Applicants may submit additional letters of recommendation, recent publications, or information about recent activities. Updated transcripts should be sent as soon as they become available."[3]

University of Virginia School of Medicine

"If they are holding an offer at a school that begins before Pritzker, then they should let us know how close to the start date of that other school they would be willing and able to consider an offer from us. So, for example, if they're starting at a school on July 1st and they decide that it would really make their life just too difficult if we made an offer after June 1st to them, that they really could not accept an offer from us at that point, then they should let us know that June 1st is the last that they could hear from Pritzker. So that's one way that they can control getting the decision from us. And then our committee will be very honest and will give them the best decision we can at the date that they say."[8]

Sylvia Robertson
Assistant Dean for Admissions at the University of Chicago Pritzker School of Medicine

----

"Please note that the admissions office staff will not disclose the number of applicants on the waitlist. In addition, we cannot make predictions as to the movement of the waitlist or an applicant's chances of admission in a given season so please keep this in mind if you contact the admissions office… It is not necessary to submit additional letters of recommendation, letters of reference, etc., as these will not influence an applicant's place on the waitlist. The Office of Admissions does encourage waitlisted applicants to periodically contact the admissions office reaffirming their interest in the UVM College of Medicine; please do so via email to medadmissions@uvm.edu."[9]

University of Vermont School of Medicine

"NYMC does not have a ranked wait list. If a position in the class becomes available to a wait listed applicant, ALL files will be reviewed. It is important for all applicants to keep their files updated with any additional information during the year."[10]

New York Medical College

Rule # 66   **There's no telling when you might hear from the Admissions Committee. Some applicants have been accepted on the day of orientation.**

While positions may become available throughout the season, movement tends to accelerate after May 15. After May 15, applicants are not permitted to hold multiple acceptances. If May 15 comes and goes and you remain on the wait list, you still have a chance. There's no way to predict when that call might come through.

"All Alternate List candidates are kept under consideration until the first day of orientation or until an applicant matriculates at another medical school, whichever comes first," writes the University of Virginia School of Medicine.[3] According to Sylvia Robertson, Assistant Dean of Admissions, the University of Chicago Pritzker School of Medicine operates in a similar manner. "In terms of how late in the year you can get an offer from Pritzker? To be honest, it's the day orientation begins, and this year that's August 5th. That's very unusual, but it has happened. And so that's the truthful answer."[8]

Decide now how you'll respond if the call does come through. Typically, an admissions officer will phone with an offer of acceptance, and they'll expect an answer, sometimes immediately.

Admissions Officers Speak...

"To make the best decision under pressure, you need to be prepared. We suggest the following steps. Make a list that includes every school where you have been wait-listed, and if you are currently holding an acceptance, include that school as well. Make a list of the factors that are most important to you in choosing between or among schools. Gather whatever information you need to compare the schools in terms of the factors that are important to you...Rank-order your list of schools from most preferred to least preferred."[1]

Tufts University School of Medicine

Rule # 67   **If you're on the wait list, make sure you're available at all times.**

Immediately notify schools if there are any changes in your contact information. Since you'll never know if and when your name will be called, ensure easy availability. This can pose a problem for wait listed applicants who are scheduled to travel in the spring and summer. If you'll be overseas, communicate this to all schools where you've been wait listed. "Please notify us of your plans via email," writes the George Washington University School of Medicine. "Include the dates when you will be unavailable (start and end dates) and if possible, the contact information for an alternative person who you've elected to make the decision on your behalf. Please include in the email, the person's full name, their relationship to you, their contact information and a statement saying that you designate this person to make the decision on your behalf."[4]

Admissions Officers Speak...

"Should you be selected from the Alternate List, it is imperative that we have a phone number where you can be reached. If you will be outside the reach of the telephone communications for any period of time, please send us a letter with the name and daytime phone number of someone who has the authority to accept or decline an offer for you."[3]

University of Virginia School of Medicine

"Update your contact information as soon as possible if there are any changes to your address, phone numbers, or email."[11]

University of North Carolina School of Medicine

References

[1]Tufts University School of Medicine. Available at: http://md.tufts.edu/Admissions/Info-for-Interviewed-Applicants/Wait-List-FAQs. Accessed March 23, 2013.

[2]Emory University School of Medicine. Available at: http://med.emory.edu/main/education/admissions/md/faq.html#After_Applying_to_Emory4. Accessed March 3, 2013.

[3]University of Virginia School of Medicine. Available at: http://www.medicine.virginia.edu/education/medical-students/admissions/old-site-2010-2012-july/som-admissions-requirements/acceptance-alternates-page. Accessed March 14, 2013.

[4]George Washington University School of Medicine. Available at: http://smhs.gwumc.edu/mdprograms/admissions/faqs/2012alternatelist/. Accessed March 3, 2013.

[5]Northwestern University Feinberg School of Medicine. Available at: http://www.feinberg.northwestern.edu/diversity/docs/Premed%20Tips%20and%20Advice%202011.pdf. Accessed March 3, 2013.

[6]Reflections of a Former Admissions Dean. Available at: web.jhu.edu/prepro/Forms/Trabilsy.Admissions.Dean.doc. Accessed February 22, 2013.

[7]Creighton University School of Medicine. Available at: http://medicine.creighton.edu/hostcommittee/faq.html. Accessed March 2, 2013.

[8]University of Chicago Pritzker School of Medicine. Available at: http://pritzkerpodcast.com/2010/05/10/31-waitlist-dynamics/#more-636. Accessed March 3, 2013.

[9]University of Vermont School of Medicine. Available at: http://www.uvm.edu/medicine/admissions/?Page=waitlistacceptance.html&SM=applysubmenu.html. Accessed March 4, 2013.

[10]New York Medical College. Available at: http://www.nymc.edu/Academics/SchoolOfMedicine/Admissions/FrequentlyAskedQuestions.html. Accessed March 24, 2013.

[11]University of North Carolina School of Medicine. Available at: http://www.med.unc.edu/admit/admissions-process. Accessed March 14, 2013.

Chapter 12

Acceptance

Rule # 68   **Adhere to all deadlines for accepting an offer.**

You'd expect that any student receiving an admissions letter would respond right away. For students weighing one offer versus another, though, it's easy to delay responding.

Understand that schools usually include a deadline with their offer. Failure to follow the school's instructions may lead to the offer being rescinded. "Applicants must respond in a timely manner to offers of acceptance to the School of Medicine," writes the University of Maryland. "Applicants will usually have three weeks from the date of the letter of acceptance to respond to the School of Medicine's offer of admission. Failure to respond will result in the withdrawal of the letter of acceptance."[1]

Rule # 69   **Offers of medical school admission can be rescinded.**

An offer of acceptance can be rescinded if the school later learns that the student misrepresented himself in some way. "Any discrepancy between the information reported during the application process and information discovered during any background check while a student at the School of Medicine, as well as any new information or incidents that occur or are reported subsequent to the application for admission, may be grounds for rescinding the acceptance or dismissal from the School of Medicine," writes the Georgetown University School of Medicine.[2]

Handling an Offer of Acceptance

Follow all instructions related to the offer of acceptance. The AAMC recommends that: [3]

- "In fairness to other applicants, when an applicant has made a decision, prior to May 15, April 30 for M.D.-Ph.D. applicants, not to attend a medical school or program that has made an offer of acceptance, the applicant **promptly** withdraw his or her application from that (those) other school(s) or program(s) by written correspondence delivered by regular or electronic methods.

- By May 15 of the matriculation year (April 15 for schools whose first day of class is on or before July 30), April 30 for M.D.-Ph.D. programs, each applicant who has received an offer of acceptance from more than one school or program choose the specific school or program at which the applicant prefers to enroll and withdraw his or her application, by written correspondence delivered by regular or electronic methods, from all other schools or programs from which acceptance offers have been received.

- Immediately upon enrollment in, or initiation of an orientation program immediately prior to enrollment at, a U.S. or Canadian school or program, each applicant withdraw his or her application from consideration at all other schools or programs at which he or she remains under consideration."

Examples include:

- Falsification of MCAT scores and the academic transcript are two examples of misrepresentation. Since these components of the application are transmitted directly to medical schools by official organizations, in practice this rarely happens.

- More common is embellishment, exaggeration, or frank dishonesty in relation to work experiences, extracurricular activities, community service, or research. Medical schools reserve the right to revoke an admission offer if such information comes to light.

Many schools require that accepted applicants undergo a criminal background check. Failure to comply will lead to withdrawal of the offer. In 2009, the AAMC reported that these checks revealed "seven felonies, 382 misdemeanors, and 67 other-than-honorable military discharges."[4] An offer may also be rescinded if the check reveals a criminal offense or violation that was not truthfully disclosed in the medical school application. "Have schools not matriculated students they accepted because of background checks? The answer is absolutely yes," said Dr. Henry Sondheimer, AAMC Senior Director of Student Affairs and Student Programs.[4]

Students accepted into medical school are expected to continue to perform well in their college coursework. Deterioration in academic performance, manifested by poor or failing grades, will be cause for concern. All schools have prerequisites, and admission may be revoked if there is failure to complete the necessary coursework. Schools also expect that students will graduate on time.

Admissions Officers Speak...

"After acceptance, an applicant is expected to complete his/her proposed educational program, maintain the same level of scholarship and continue to demonstrate the high moral standards required for entrance to the College of Medicine... If an applicant's circumstances change from what could have been reasonably expected from the application file, i.e., fails or withdraws from a course, has a failing grade, drops out of a program, fails to obtain a degree or a major or minor, that they indicated they would receive, or in general does not sustain the level of academic achievement upon which the Admissions Committee made their initial decision, then the facts of the application are no longer valid and the acceptance will be reviewed and possibly withdrawn."[5]

University of Arkansas for the Medical Sciences

"We would not automatically withdraw our offer if a hit came up. We do reserve the right to institute certain actions, and we try to have those actions be consistent with what we would do for house staff."[4]

Wayne M. Samuelson, M.D.
Senior Associate Dean at the University of Utah School of Medicine

----

"What has become a concern is a pattern of behavior that may not be classified as violent per se, but could still be considered worrisome. Usually, this pattern means a record of substance abuse, or a failure to self-disclose an incident, which we say is tantamount to applicant falsification."[4]

Steven T. Case, Ph.D.
Associate Dean for Admissions at the University of Mississippi School of Medicine

----

"Applicants' explanations for criminal offenses have ranged from dismissive to acceptance of responsibility for an event that served as a life-altering experience resulting in personal growth. Some applicants have used these situations to demonstrate the maturity to overcome isolated lapses in judgment and the tenacity to escape negative influences. What was unanticipated to some degree was the number of applicants who failed to self-disclose incidents that appear in their criminal history for reasons ranging from misunderstanding complexities of the legal system (e.g., not realizing that payment of a fine constitutes a guilty plea or assuming that records would be expunged without further intervention) to apparent lapses in memory."[6]

James Kleshinski, M.D.
Associate Dean of Admissions at University of Toledo College of Medicine

Rule # 70   Prepare for Day # 1 of medical school

In the weeks or months left before starting medical school, address or complete the following:

- Think about summer plans
- Hunt for housing
- Apply for financial aid as early as possible
- Consider alternative sources for financing your medical education
- Submit final university transcript
- Keep contact information updated, as schools will send important communications
- Complete immunization requirements to avoid a delay in matriculation
- Complete background check

Admissions Officers Speak...

"The financial aid deadline for incoming students is April 13th. Award decisions for on-time, completed applications will be processed and mailed out by May 15th. The financial aid deadline for continuing students is May 15th. On-time applications will be processed and mailed out in July. Timely submission of all application materials is essential as financial aid decisions are based on financial need and availability of funds: late applicants could jeopardize their access to limited sources of aid."[7]

Harvard Medical School

"It is very important that you file your Free Application for Federal Student Aid (FAFSA) before the filing deadline. Since it is possible that some students are not interested in applying for financial assistance, the FAFSA form is not part of the admissions materials. You may request a FAFSA application from the Office of Student Financial Services after January 1st. You may also submit your application on the Internet at www.fafsa.ed.gov. For University-based funding, the deadline for application receipt at the Federal Processor is MARCH 1st preceding the September term."[8]

Temple University School of Medicine

References

[1]University of Maryland School of Medicine. Available at:
http://medschool.umaryland.edu/admissions/appres.asp. Accessed March 3, 2013.

[2]Georgetown University School of Medicine. Available at:
http://som.georgetown.edu/docs/Criminal%20Background%20Check.pdf. Accessed March 3, 2013.

[3]Association of American Medical Colleges. Available at:
https://www.aamc.org/students/applying/recommendations/applicants/. Accessed March 2, 2013.

[4]Association of American Medical Colleges. Available at:
https://www.aamc.org/newsroom/reporter/july09/75704/july09_background.html. Accessed March 30, 2013.

[5]University of Arkansas for the Medical Sciences. Available at:
http://www.uams.edu/com/comcat/2011-2012_Cat_Sects/2012_com_catalog_For-Applicant.pdf. Accessed March 24, 2013.

[6]Kleshinski J, Case S, Davis D, Heinrich G, Witzburg R. Criminal background checks for entering medical students. *Acad Med* 2011; 86 (7): 795-8.

[7]Harvard Medical School. Available at: http://hms.harvard.edu/content/faq. Accessed March 3, 2013.

[8]Temple University School of Medicine. Available at:
http://www.temple.edu/sfs/med/applying.htm. Accessed March 3, 2013.

Chapter 13

Osteopathic Medical School Interview

Rule # 71   The osteopathic interview requires additional specific preparation.

By the end of the decade, over 25% of all medical students graduating from U.S. schools on a yearly basis will be DOs.[1]

Therefore, many applicants will apply to both allopathic and osteopathic medical schools. The DO degree, signifying **Doctor of Osteopathic Medicine**, is granted to graduates of osteopathic schools. While the bulk of preparation will be the same for both types of medical schools, an osteopathic interview does require some specific additional preparation.

Are you familiar with the osteopathic philosophy and approach? Do you really want to attend an osteopathic school? These are among the questions osteopathic medical schools seek to answer through the interview process. "Students seeking admissions must demonstrate understanding of and sincere interest in osteopathic medicine," writes the Arizona College of Osteopathic Medicine.[2]

Did you know...

"Interviews at osteopathic medical schools are particularly important. Osteopathic medicine has a rich history of producing passionate, empathetic, considerate, altruistic, well-balanced physicians. These are individuals who not only demonstrate academic excellence, but who are also dedicated to the humane delivery of medical care under the auspices of the osteopathic medical philosophy. Osteopathic medical schools take great pride in seeking future physicians who have developed listening skills, communication skills, a high level of ethics and a strong sense of social responsibility. Osteopathic medical schools actively seek those students who are committed to osteopathic medicine as a career and a lifestyle. The admission interview can be very helpful in identifying these attributes."[3]

American Association of Colleges of Osteopathic Medicine (Osteopathic Medical College Information Book)

Did you know...

"If you are selected for an interview, prepare carefully. Examine your motives for pursuing a degree in osteopathic medicine and be prepared to relate your experience to your goals...The interviewers will ask questions about your academic strengths, interests and your motivation towards a career in osteopathic medicine."[4]

Des Moines University College of Osteopathic Medicine

Tip # 28

If you've shadowed an osteopathic physician, plan to discuss how the experience has informed you about the philosophy, mission, and principles of osteopathic medicine.

Rule # 72   **Learn the specifics of osteopathic manipulative medicine.**

Osteopathic manipulative medicine (OMM) is the key feature that differentiates osteopathic from allopathic medical education.

What is Osteopathic Manipulative Medicine?

"DOs receive extra training in manipulating the musculoskeletal system - your body's interconnected system of nerves, muscles and bones that make up two-thirds of your body mass. This training in osteopathic manipulative medicine (OMM) provides osteopathic physicians with a better understanding of how an injury or illness in one part of the body can affect another...With OMM, DOs use their hands to diagnose injury and illness and to encourage your body's natural tendency toward good health. By combining all other medical procedures with OMM, DOs offer their patients the most comprehensive care available in medicine today."[5]

Philadelphia College of Osteopathic Medicine

Considerable time is spent in the curriculum on OMM, and OMM is a point of pride for many osteopathic educators. Critics of OMM argue that the available research supporting its use isn't strong enough, based on lack of rigor with respect to methodology and design. Over the past decade, there's been renewed vigor among the osteopathic medical community to provide evidence of OMM's clinical efficacy through robust research studies. This led the Texas College of Osteopathic Medicine at the University of North Texas to establish the Osteopathic Research Center, and similar initiatives have been launched at other schools.

Therefore, you shouldn't be surprised if interviewers assess your awareness of the basic principles of OMM and your willingness to embrace it. In a survey of nearly 3,000 students who applied to osteopathic medical schools in 2009, researchers found that only 29% felt that osteopathic philosophy was an important factor in deciding whether to enroll.[6] "A lack of enthusiasm or understanding of osteopathic philosophy might be correlated with a lack of interest in pursuing a career in medicine that incorporates OMM and OMT [osteopathic manipulative treatment]," wrote Dr. Raddy Ramos, a faculty member in the Department of Neuroscience at the New York College of Osteopathic Medicine.[7]

Rule # 73   **Demonstrate how your background ties in with the school's mission.**

Osteopathic medical schools are committed to primary care. Research indicates that osteopathic schools graduate more physicians who pursue careers in primary care. There's also an emphasis on caring for the underserved, and some osteopathic schools have excellent track records for graduating physicians who practice in rural settings.[8]

Did you know...

In one study, differences were noted in how allopathic and osteopathic physicians interacted with patients. "Osteopathic physicians were more likely than allopathic physicians to use patients' first names; explain etiologic factors to patients; and discuss social, family, and emotional impact of illnesses."[9]

Osteopathic Medical Schools Speak About Their Mission

"The Touro College of Osteopathic Medicine is committed to training osteopathic physicians, with a particular emphasis on practicing medicine in underserved communities..."[10]

"The Mission of the College of Osteopathic Medicine of the Pacific (COMP) is to prepare students to become technically competent, culturally sensitive, professional and compassionate physicians who are lifelong learners and will serve society by providing comprehensive, patient-centered healthcare with the distinctive osteopathic philosophy."[11]

"The primary goal of LECOM [Lake Erie College of Osteopathic Medicine] is to educate students to become physicians who practice within the osteopathic concept. Additionally, the college's goal is to educate and develop primary care physicians who will practice in the osteopathic tradition."[12]

"We [University of Pikeville-Kentucky College of Osteopathic Medicine] focus on producing the highest quality osteopathic physicians, to practice primary care in the rural and underserved areas of Kentucky and Appalachia."[13]

Key Points About the History of Osteopathic Medicine

- Osteopathic medicine was founded in 1874 by Dr. Andrew Taylor Still.

- Dr. Still believed that the practice of medicine in his era was ineffective and could even be harmful, and this led him to develop the new model of "osteopathy."

- In 1892, he established the first school of osteopathy in Kirksville, Missouri, and other schools were soon founded by his graduates.

- Just before the turn of the century, these new osteopathic schools formed the organization Associated Colleges of Osteopathy (the precursor to today's Association of Colleges of Osteopathic Medicine).

- In 1901, the American Osteopathic Association (AOA) was founded.

- The profession suffered harsh criticism in the early 20th century. Over the course of a century, this has changed considerably.

- By 1973, osteopathic physicians were eligible for licensure in all 50 states.

- Since the 1960s, the curriculum of osteopathic and allopathic medical schools has largely been the same, with the exception of courses in osteopathic manipulative medicine (OMM) during the first and second years with continued clinical training in this area during the third and fourth years.

- In recent years, osteopathic schools have made significant innovations in their curriculum, moving away from the traditional lecture-based approach to a mixture of lectures, small group teaching, and problem-based sessions.

- Like allopathic schools, osteopathic schools are now placing more emphasis on the integration of basic and clinical sciences during the first and second years of medical school.

- Considerable growth has occurred in the use of standardized patients and simulation as tools for instruction and evaluation.

- Opportunities for research have increased at osteopathic schools.

- More schools are offering combined degree programs (DO/PhD, DO/MBA, DO/MPH)

Shannon S, Teitelbaum H. The status and future of osteopathic medical education in the United States. *Acad Med* 2009; 84(6): 707-711.

Rule # 73   Avoid the obvious, but unfortunately common, interview errors.

AACOM has developed a list of interview don'ts. "Do not:

- Appear or be insincere during any portion of your interview.
- Try to guess what the interviewer wants to hear.
- Be afraid to discuss your successes and most positive traits.
- Make excuses for past difficulties or challenges.
- Act with a negative attitude or use a negative tone in your responses.
- Arrive under-prepared or unprepared for this discussion."[14]

References

[1]Gevitz N. The transformation of osteopathic medical education. *Acad Med* 2009; 84 (6): 701 – 6.

[2]Arizona College of Osteopathic Medicine. Available at: http://www.midwestern.edu/programs-and-admission/az-osteopathic-medicine.html. Accessed April 1, 2013.

[3]American Association of Colleges of Osteopathic Medicine (Osteopathic Medical College Information Book). Available at: http://www.aacom.org/resources/bookstore/cib/Documents/2013cib/2013CIB_whole_we b.pdf. Accessed March 3, 2013.

[4]Des Moines University College of Osteopathic Medicine. Available at: http://www.dmu.edu/do/how-to-apply/interview-day/. Accessed March 25, 2013.

[5]Philadelphia College of Osteopathic Medicine. Available at: http://www.pcom.edu/general_information/Osteopathic_Medicine/Osteopathic_Medicine .html. Accessed March 26, 2013.

[6]Meron J, Levitan T. 2009 Applicants to COCA-Accredited Osteopathic and LCME-Accredited Allopathic Medical Schools: A Survey Analysis of the 2009 AACOMAS Applicant Pool. Available at: http://www.aacom.org/resources/bookstore/Documents/AppRpt2009.pdf. Accessed January 21, 2011.

[7]Ramos R, Zhou C, Hasan M, Herrera S, Bono N, Hallas B. Understanding osteopathic medical school applicants and the class of 2014. *J Am Osteopath Assoc* 2011; 111 (3): 174-5.

[8]Mullan F, Chen C, Petterson S, Kolsky G, Spagnola M. The social mission of medical education: ranking the schools. *Ann Intern Med* 2010; 152 (12): 804-11.

[9]Carey T, Motyka T, Garrett J, Keller R. Do osteopathic physicians differ in patient interaction from allopathic physicians? An empirically derived approach. *J Am Osteopath Assoc* 2003; 103 (7): 313-8.

[10]Tuoro College of Osteopathic Medicine. Available at: http://www.touro.edu/med/mission.html. Accessed March 3, 2013.

[11]College of Osteopathic Medicine of the Pacific. Available at: http://www.westernu.edu/osteopathy-mission. Accessed March 3, 2013.

[12]Lake Erie College of Osteopathic Medicine. Available at: http://lecom.edu/mission.php. Accessed March 3, 2013.

[13]Pikeville-Kentucky College of Osteopathic Medicine. Available at: http://www.upike.edu/College-of-Osteopathic-Medicine/dean. Accessed March 4, 2013.

[14]American Association of Colleges of Osteopathic Medicine. Available at: http://www.aacom.org/resources/bookstore/cib/Documents/2012cib/2012cib-p24-25.pdf. Accessed March 30, 2013.

Chapter 14

The Preclinical Years of Medical School

Note: The following chapter is excerpted from the book – Success in Medical School: Insider Advice for the Preclinical Years

The preclinical years of medical school are extremely challenging, and that may be understating the reality. At one medical school, faculty assigned "29,239 pages of reading for the 12 basic science modules that were scheduled during 71 weeks."[1]

As you begin med school, you'll hear a lot of advice.

- "If you thought the MCAT was tough, wait until you see the USMLE."

- "The material it took you a semester to cover in college? You'll get through that in a week in med school."

- "If you want to go down the ROAD, you'd better start planning now, figure out your research, and make your connections early - and you'll have to maximize that first summer off." [ROAD = Radiology, Ophthalmology, Anesthesiology, Dermatology]

There is at least some truth in every one of those statements.

Medical school is extremely challenging, and not just in the ways that you'd assume. The sheer volume of material covered is staggering. And most importantly, unlike in some of your college courses, much of it builds upon prior material. Your study methods therefore have to ensure long-term retention. In Chapter 2 [Preclinical Courses], you'll hear advice from students, faculty, and experts, as well as the results of research, on how to learn such a large volume of material, and how to ensure retention. In one study, researchers found that "in general, study skills are stronger predictors of first-semester total grades than aptitude as measured by the MCAT and undergraduate GPA."[2] The importance of long-term retention of basic science material is emphasized by the United States Medical Licensing Exam. The USMLE Step 1 exam is taken at the end of the preclinical years, and your score on this single exam can influence the course of your career. The exam tests your ability to take the basic science material covered over two years in medical school and apply it to clinical situations. In Chapter 3, you'll learn about the exam itself, as well as the most common mistakes that students make when preparing. You'll learn about resources that can aid your preparation, and you'll learn about the importance of this single score in the residency application process. Chapter 4 provides specifics about the COMLEX Level 1 exam. This exam, taken by osteopathic students, is of similar importance.

While mastering such a large amount of basic science material is extremely challenging, unfortunately that's not enough. Your skills in the hands-on art and science of patient care will be critical. Learning about a disease and its manifestations in the classroom does not ensure that you'll know what to do when faced with a patient in the clinic. It is widely believed that physicians' examination skills have deteriorated over the years. While a number of factors may be responsible, it is believed that clinical skills training may play a role. In fact, if you don't adequately learn certain skills and techniques during your preclinical courses [Introduction to Clinical Medicine or Physical Diagnosis], you may never learn them, not even during clerkships. "Surveys have indicated that less than 16% of attending time may be spent at the patient's side."[3] This has important ramifications for patient care. When researchers observed interns and residents, they noted frequent errors in physical exam technique, including improper use of instruments. In Chapters 5 [Taking a Patient History] and 6 [Physical Examination], you'll learn how to make the most of your history and physical exam education.

The challenges of the preclinical years extend beyond the well-known. Chapters 11 and 12 provide some startling statistics on medical student well-being and issues of professionalism. Physicians are challenged on a daily basis with the stressors of clinical patient care, and the coping mechanisms and buffering strategies you develop now, as a preclinical student, will be vital throughout the course of your career.

Several chapters highlight the significant opportunities available to medical students. Medical schools, organizations, and individual medical students have all been able to impact medical practice or their communities in significant ways, and their accomplishments are inspiring. Chapters on Community Service, Extracurricular Activities, and Research serve as a guide on how to get started, and highlight the numerous opportunities for preclinical students to become involved and thus have the opportunity to make a meaningful impact. Chapters on teaching, awards, and international experiences provide details on further opportunities.

Throughout these challenges, you do have to consider your future. As the residency selection process for certain fields becomes ever more competitive, students who have at least started strategizing early in their education will be at an advantage. Chapter 16 [Choosing a Specialty] reviews the process of strategizing in detail. For the most competitive specialties, great grades and high USMLE scores are not enough. You'll need great letters of recommendation and support from faculty advocates. In Chapter 10 [Mentoring], you'll learn ways in which preclinical students can approach established faculty members and obtain their assistance and guidance. You'll also need additional distinctions. Most applicants to the competitive specialties will have performed research, and many will have publications or presentations to their name. Chapter 7 [Research] reviews the process, demonstrates how students can begin, details what to seek in a research project, and provides specifics on research, publication, and presentation opportunities available to medical students. Some residency programs also seek additional factors of distinction, such as involvement in extracurricular activities, evidence of leadership, and commitment to service. In "Choosing a Specialty," you'll learn how to start the process of exploring a specialty. The chapter also includes specifics about identifying research opportunities, locating specialty-specific mentors, seeking out community service projects within the field, and other specialty-specific opportunities.

Throughout the next 300+ pages, we'll review each of these areas in detail. From grades and exams, to the art of patient care, to strategizing for your career, you'll learn specific, detailed information relevant to the preclinical medical student. These reviews and recommendations are based on the experiences of students, residents, and faculty, as well as a thorough review of the scientific literature in the areas of medical education and patient care. This combination of insider information and evidence-based advice is utilized to help you gain the strongest foundation as you face the challenges of medical school. Your goal is to become the best doctor possible, and that process begins on day one of medical school.

Preclinical courses/grades

At one medical school, faculty assigned "29,239 pages of reading."[1]

The core of this chapter centers on one vital question related to that startling fact. How can a student read and retain such a large volume of information?

In Chapter 2, you'll learn what students, faculty, and experts advise on how to get through the mountain of material a med student is expected to master. The most common mistake that med students seem to make? They assume that studying longer and harder will be enough to succeed.

It's not.

The students who are able to excel in medical school have learned how to effectively strategize and utilize the techniques of active learning, among other study strategies. Reading and highlighting material, even multiple times, won't be enough to ensure the long-term retention that medical school requires.

Upperclassmen at the University of Alabama Birmingham School of Medicine offer the following advice to new students: "The material is rarely difficult; there is just a mountain's worth to cover. A normal medical school exam seems like a cumulative final in the most strenuous science course you took in undergraduate. You simply cannot learn the material overnight or with one quick read-through of the scripts."[4]

Prior to med school, you no doubt heard about the heavy academic workload. The volume of material to be covered is truly enormous, and while students expect this, it doesn't fully sink in until the first week when you receive lecture materials, syllabi, and books. Consider the following comments made by new medical students:

- "I was worried that I wouldn't be able to keep up."

- "What scared me most was the amount of information I was asked to master."

- "It was all so overwhelming. How could I possibly learn it all? After all, I could barely carry it."

While the preclinical curriculum will vary among medical schools, most schools will focus on the same core subjects. In 2006, the International Association of Medical Science Educators convened a group of respected medical educators to answer some key questions about the role and value of the basic sciences in medical education.[5] The educators identified eight sciences - anatomy, physiology, biochemistry, neuroscience, microbiology, immunology, pathology, and pharmacology – as "vital foundations of medical practice." Also deemed critical to a strong foundation was education in behavioral sciences, genetics, epidemiology, molecular biology, and biostatistics.

Given the significant challenges of learning and retaining this much material, what is the best way for students to approach their preclinical courses? In this chapter, you'll learn the differences between top and average performers, and you'll learn about study strategies that have led to success. In one study, researchers found that "in general, study skills are stronger predictors of first-semester total grades than aptitude as measured by the MCAT and undergraduate GPA."[2] You'll learn about common mistakes that students make when approaching the basic sciences, and how to avoid those mistakes. You'll also hear suggestions from students who have successfully navigated these challenges.

USMLE Step 1 Exam

The USMLE Step 1 exam is a critical factor in the residency selection process. While there's a lot that can be said about preparation for this exam, it can be summarized in one sentence: typical study methods don't work for this exam.

To become an allopathic physician with the license to practice in the United States, you must pass the three-part United States Medical Licensing Exam, referred to as the USMLE. Medical students typically take the first part of the USMLE (Step 1 exam) at the end of the second year of medical school. The Step 1 score is also an important criterion used by residency programs in the selection process. In a 2006 survey of over 1,200 residency program directors across 21 medical specialties, the USMLE Step 1 score was found to be the second most important residency selection factor, following only grades in required clerkships.[6]

In competitive specialties such as dermatology, plastic surgery, ophthalmology, otolaryngology, radiology, neurosurgery, orthopedic surgery, and urology, many programs have a cut-off, or threshold, USMLE Step 1 score. Highly sought-after programs in less competitive specialties may also have threshold scores. Applicants who score above the cut-off are considered for interviews. Those below the cut-off may be removed from consideration.

"Many medical students that we have talked to underestimate the amount of clinical material on the USMLE Step 1 examination.... Furthermore, many students also leave the exam feeling somewhat intimidated regarding the clinical slant of how the basic science material is tested." - Drs. Tao Le and Chirag Amin, authors of the popular book *First Aid for the USMLE Step 1*.[7]

The National Board of Medical Examiners (NBME), which administers the exam, states that the USMLE Step 1 exam "assesses whether you can understand and apply important concepts of the sciences to the practice of medicine, with special emphasis on the principles and mechanisms underlying health, disease, and modes of therapy."[8]

While strong factual knowledge is necessary for exam success, most questions seek to determine your ability to apply basic science knowledge to clinical problems, rather than regurgitate isolated facts. In a recent posting at www.usmle.org, the National Board of Medical Examiners announced a further reduction in the number of Step 1 items presented without a clinical vignette.

This focus on clinical applications, rather than rote memorization, makes the USMLE a distinctive and challenging exam for most students. Adding to the challenge is the amount of information that students are expected to master. The content of the exam is drawn from the following disciplines: Anatomy, Physiology, Biochemistry, Pathology, Pharmacology, Microbiology, Behavioral Sciences, and Nutrition/Genetics/Aging. The Step 1 exam, therefore, covers information that requires 2 years of medical school to learn. Most students devote a 6 week block of time to review material and prepare for this exam. Cramming, obviously, won't work.

In Chapter 3, you'll learn the basics of the Step 1 exam. What material does it cover, and what material do you need to review? Does the curriculum offered by your school provide adequate preparation? Most schools adhere to a disciplines-based, organ-based, or problem-based curriculum, or a combination thereof. Researchers have utilized AAMC [Association of American Medical Colleges] data to determine what effects, if any, the curricular approach had on USMLE scores.

What are the mistakes that students make when preparing for the exam? Dr. Judy Schwenker, Kaplan's Curriculum Director, has identified the five most common mistakes students make when preparing for the Step 1 exam.[9] These include passive studying, insufficient practice with questions, memorizing without understanding the material, inappropriate test day strategies, and misreading or misinterpreting questions. In this chapter, we provide suggestions on exam preparation that avoid these common mistakes.

How should you study for an exam of this importance that's so distinct from other exams? Drs. Helen Loeser and Maxine Papadakis, Deans at the UCSF School of Medicine, advise: "Use active learning methods as you integrate your knowledge and apply basic science information to clinical vignettes."[10] Research has shown that active learning leads to better long-term retention of information and easier retrieval of information when needed. In this chapter you'll learn about techniques of active learning, and resources that can aid in your preparation.

COMLEX Level 1 Exam

For osteopathic students, the route to licensure requires passage of the three-level COMLEX. These parts include COMLEX Level 1, COMLEX Level 2 (further subdivided into Level 2 Cognitive Evaluation or CE and Level 2 Performance Evaluation or PE), and COMLEX Level 3. Osteopathic students typically take the COMLEX Level 1 exam near the end of the second year, while both components of the Level 2 exam are taken in the fourth year.

According to the National Board of Osteopathic Medical Examiners (NBOME), which administers the exam, the COMLEX Level 1 exam "emphasizes the scientific concepts and principles necessary for understanding the mechanisms of health, medical problems and disease processes."[11] Information about the content of the exam is available at their website (see Bulletin of Information), and should be reviewed carefully. In contrast to the USMLE, the COMLEX examination incorporates osteopathic principles, including the use of osteopathic manipulative treatment.

Like the USMLE, the COMLEX Level 1 exam is used by programs in the residency selection process. This process can be divided into two phases – screening and ranking. In the screening phase, programs whittle down a large applicant pool into a smaller group. The members of this group will be offered interview invitations. The COMLEX Level 1 score is frequently used in the screening process by allopathic and osteopathic residency programs. In 2010, a survey of several thousand allopathic residency program directors representing multiple specialties was performed by the National Resident Matching Program. The survey found that the Level 1 score was the factor used most commonly in the screening process.[12]

In competitive specialties such as dermatology, plastic surgery, ophthalmology, otolaryngology, radiology, neurosurgery, orthopedic surgery, and urology, many programs have a cut-off or threshold COMLEX Level 1 score. Highly sought-after programs in less competitive specialties may also have threshold scores. Applicants who score above the cut-off are considered for interviews. Those below the cut-off may be removed from consideration.

In this chapter, you'll learn about how the COMLEX Level 1 score is used by residency programs in the selection process. You'll learn about ways to identify your strengths and weaknesses, as well as indicators that you may be at risk for a low COMLEX score. You'll also hear tips to help you prepare for the exam. For example, the NBOME offers students the opportunity to take the Comprehensive Osteopathic Medical Self-Assessment Exam (COMSAE) as a means to assess readiness for the COMLEX Level 1 exam. The format and structure of the Phase 1 COMSAE resembles that of the Level 1 exam. Furthermore, scoring and reporting of the two exams are similar. In a study performed by the NBOME, the organization found that the two scores were highly related. While candidates can take a timed or untimed COMSAE, the data seems to suggest that the timed exam has higher self-assessment value.

While we review the role of the COMLEX in the residency selection process, in this chapter you'll learn that this score, by itself, may not be sufficient for all residency programs. In recent years, an increasing number of osteopathic students have applied to residency programs approved by the Accreditation Council for Graduate Medical Education (ACGME). According to Drs. Cummings and Sefcik, Deans at the Michigan State University College of Osteopathic Medicine, "in 2006, more than two of every three DOs [6,629 of 9,618] in postdoctoral training were in an ACGME program."[13] Since ACGME-accredited programs are less familiar with the COMLEX score, these programs often recommend that osteopathic applicants take the USMLE Step 1 exam. This allows programs to make easier comparisons between MD and DO student applicants.

Taking a Patient History

It's well-known that the transition between learning about medicine in the classroom and actually applying that knowledge in the care of real patients is quite challenging. Studies have confirmed that students have high levels of stress and anxiety as they move from the preclinical to clinical years of medical school.[14]

Clinical skills, including the history and physical exam, are often mentioned as a major struggle in the transition period. One student described her discomfort. "I felt uncomfortable talking to the patient and trying to come up with methodical ways of asking questions and making sure I didn't miss things, not just jumping around all over the place."[15]

Traditionally, preclinical students have had limited contact with patients. In recent years, however, schools have placed new emphasis on clinical skills training in early medical education. Some schools now even introduce students to patients as soon as the first week or month of medical school.

Medical organizations have also recognized the importance of an early emphasis on clinical skills, including communication. In 2004, the Institute of Medicine made the acquisition and development of communication skills a top priority during medical education. That same year, the National Board of Medical Examiners (NBME) began requiring students to take a clinical skills exam (USMLE Step 2 CS) as a means to assess competence in communication. The hope is that through education on effective communication, students will be better versed in how to listen, question, counsel, and motivate patients.

Your efforts to improve communication skills will also impact your clerkship performance. In a survey of clerkship directors, while over 95% felt that students require an intermediate to advanced level of communication skills, approximately 30% felt that new clerkship students aren't sufficiently prepared.[16]

Medical schools evaluate communication skills in different ways. One is through comprehensive clinical skills assessment using standardized patients. Researchers have interviewed faculty members responsible for helping those students who don't perform well in these assessments. Some of the issues have focused on patient histories.[17] "Many low-scoring students focused prematurely, failing to ask open-ended questions or adequately characterize the chief complaint. Respondents also observed students being too focused on the history of present illness, omitting or incompletely exploring the pertinent past medical, social, or family history, particularly as they related to the chief complaint." Some students failed to explore the patient's perspective on the illness. The authors wrote that "these students treated standardized patients as symptoms or diagnoses rather than as people with feelings or concerns."

In Chapter 5, you'll learn how to make the most of your clinical skills education. You'll learn about the deficiencies that have been documented in the physician-patient communication literature with respect to history taking, and how educators have developed benchmarks to guide medical students in their acquisition of important communication skills. As you develop your history taking skills, you'll learn how to use these benchmarks, solicit feedback to assess your progress, and reflect on your own performance in order to improve your skills.

Physical Examination

Although 80% of diagnoses are made based on the history and physical examination, evidence indicates that the physical exam skills of physicians today are inadequate. It is widely believed that physicians' examination skills have deteriorated over the years. While advances in technology, including laboratory testing and radiologic imaging, are partly to blame for this decline, clinical skills training during medical school and residency are also factors. According to Dr. Sal Mangione, Director of the Physical Diagnosis Curriculum at Jefferson Medical College, too little time is spent during medical school learning these skills. "Surveys have indicated that less than 16% of attending time may be spent at the patient's side."[18]

Physical exam skills have important, obvious ramifications for patient care, and the education you receive in this area during medical school is critical. If you don't learn certain skills at this stage of your education, you may never have the opportunity to do so. In one study, researchers observed interns and residents, and noted frequent errors in physical exam technique.[19] Errors included improper manual technique or use of instruments. The authors asserted that these errors resulted from a failure to learn the necessary psychomotor skills during the preclinical years.

In the real world of medicine, these deficiencies in skills have serious consequences. In a study of interns and residents on a general medicine service, at least one serious physical exam error was made for nearly two-thirds of the patients examined. The errors included failure to detect splenomegaly or focal neurological signs, findings that once discovered led to significant changes in diagnosis and treatment.[20]

While clinical courses such as "Introduction to Clinical Medicine" and "Physical Diagnosis" teach these skills, this is one area where students cannot rely on passive learning. In Chapter 6, you'll learn how to make the most of your physical exam education. These skills aren't easy to learn. While a recent study showed that third-year med students felt quite confident about their ability to measure blood pressure, students were significantly less confident in their ability to assess retinal vasculature, detect a thyroid nodule, or measure jugular venous pressure.[21]

You'll also learn the importance of soliciting preceptor feedback. If errors aren't picked up at this stage of your education, they may never be. While you might expect that your future residents or attendings would be able to correct your performance, the literature has shown that students on clerkships often aren't observed while performing physical exams. They are typically assumed to already possess the necessary skills.

The chapter also addresses other facets of physical exams, including the patient's comfort. You'll learn how to approach an often uncomfortable situation in a manner that most reassures the patient. In the article "Learning to Doctor," Conrad aptly describes the concerns of students:[22]

Students tell patients twice their age to get undressed, and then cross conventional barriers of interpersonal space to inspect the intimacies of their bodies. In addition to anxiety about doing it right, students frequently must deal with their own reactions to their patient as well as discomforting feelings of being invasive.

Research

In a presentation to medical students titled "Research in Medical School," Dr. Daniel West discussed reasons why students should consider involvement in research. Dr. West noted that participation in research allows medical students to explore a specialty in more depth, enhance critical thinking and other related skills, assess suitability for a career in academic medicine, and strengthen credentials for residency positions.[23] Medical students recognize these benefits as well. In a survey of students at three medical schools, 83% agreed that participation in research was valuable within their medical education.[24]

In Chapter 7, we'll discuss these benefits in more depth. There are significant benefits to participation in research, and while barriers exist, many medical students are able to overcome these barriers, enhance their own skills and education, and make contributions to the scientific literature.

Research training leads to better critical thinking skills. The ability to critically appraise the literature is essential to the practice of evidence-based medicine. The University of Arizona College of Medicine writes that "as future physicians, being able to critically read a scientific journal along with keeping abreast of new medical innovations is an important facet of practice that can profoundly impact patient outcomes."[25] In a recent article, Mayo researchers wrote about how research benefits medical students.[26] "Studies have shown that students who had conducted research during medical school reported gains in knowledge and skills in appraising the literature, analyzing data, and writing for publication, along with more positive attitudes toward future research." Students report significant benefits from learning the process of research, from conception of an idea to publication and presentation. It is important for all physicians to learn about literature review, hypothesis generation, study methodology, and data analysis.

Research also has known benefits in the residency selection process. Dr. Scott Pretorius, former Radiology Residency Program Director at the University of Pennsylvania, wrote that "in this competitive market for radiology residency slots, medical students with research backgrounds...allow themselves the opportunity to stand out in a field of increasingly highly qualified applicants. As an advisor of medical students, I routinely recommend that students intending to apply for radiology residency seek out a research mentor and undertake some kind of research project."[27] In a survey of University of Tennessee medical students, 63% reported that research experience was beneficial in helping them secure a residency position.[28]

As you're applying for residency positions, it's important to know your competition. Among dermatology applicants, nearly 95% had participated in at least one research project, with over 80% claiming at least one abstract, publication, or presentation.[29] In radiation oncology, among U.S. senior applicants, only 9 of the 152 applicants reported not having a single abstract, publication, or presentation. While it's not a prerequisite for students applying to competitive fields, a student may stand out due to their lack of any research experience in these fields.

While students recognize the benefits of research, many find the barriers to involvement daunting. Difficulty finding a research supervisor can be a significant barrier, with only 44% of students in one study reporting that it was easy to identify one.[24] In this chapter, you'll learn how to identify research opportunities at your institution. We highlight ways to identify the "right" research mentor, as well as what to discuss with potential mentors and how to evaluate potential research projects.

In evaluating research experience during medical school, residency programs will look closely at the level of your involvement. Did you merely collect data? Or were you involved through all phases of the project (design of the project, data collection, analysis of the data, and writing the manuscript)? Programs also assess your productivity. Did your work result in a tangible measure, such as an abstract, manuscript, or presentation at a meeting? For many students involved in research, a publication or presentation resulting from their work would be ideal. While this isn't always possible, in this chapter you'll learn how to approach the issue of publication and learn about journals that are targeted to medical students.

You'll also learn about possibilities for presentation, even if those opportunities aren't initiated by your research mentor. Students may seek out opportunities to present their work at local, regional, national, and international meetings. At Stanford University School of Medicine, 52% of medical students had presented at a national meeting.[30] Symposiums and meetings geared to medical student research presentations include the National Student Research Forum (NSRF), Eastern-Atlantic Student Research Forum (ESRF), and Western Student Medical Research Forum (WSMRF). The NSRF is held at the University of Texas Medical Branch in Galveston, and provides a forum for students to give either poster or oral presentations.[31] Over 30 awards are given at this annual event.

Time has been reported as a major barrier to pursuing research in medical school. Many students become involved in research in the summer between the first and second years of medical school. Opportunities for summer research may also be available for newly admitted students who haven't yet started medical school. At the Mt. Sinai School of Medicine, 54 to 65% of students participated in summer research between 2001 and 2004.[32]

Some students are interested in a more substantial research experience, and in this chapter you'll learn about some of the "year-out" opportunities available to students across the country. The Clinical Research Fellowship for Medical Students, sponsored by the Doris Duke Charitable Foundation, offers one-year fellowships at one of 12 selected institutions in the U.S. The HHMI – NIH (Howard Hughes Medical Institute - National Institutes of Health) Research Scholars Program and NIH Clinical Research Training Program allow participants the opportunity to work on the NIH campus. Research Training Fellowships through the HHMI are also available to students, and support one year of research at a variety of academic institutions. This chapter highlights a number of other opportunities that are available for students interested in more substantial research experience.

Extracurricular Activities

As in college, the learning environment in medical school extends beyond the classroom, and institutions offer valuable opportunities to participate in a variety of extracurricular activities. For example, at the Case Western Reserve University, there are over 40 medical student organizations.[33]

Involvement in these organizations provides a number of opportunities and benefits, and in Chapter 8 you'll learn more about the opportunities available. One of the most important is the further development of skills that are directly applicable to success as a physician. A few examples of vital skills in the daily life of a physician are teamwork, self-discipline, time management, and leadership, all of which are strengthened outside of the classroom through extracurricular involvement. Involvement in organizations is a way to develop and strengthen bonds with classmates, and since student organizations often have a faculty advisor or sponsor, students have extraordinary opportunities to work closely with faculty members. Such opportunities are usually unavailable to students during the preclinical years.

Some students are awarded recognition for their involvement. Every year, the American Medical Association honors 15 students with AMA Foundation Leadership Awards. These awards recognize students who have demonstrated "strong, nonclinical leadership skills in advocacy, community service, public health, and/or education."[34] Many other organizations recognize student involvement as well. When evaluating a student's contributions, organizations seek evidence of leadership, commitment, and the ability to make meaningful contributions to the goals of an organization. Some students, after reviewing the opportunities available at their school, commit to starting a new organization or founding a new chapter of a national organization. In this chapter, you'll learn what questions to ask, and what resources are available, as you review your opportunities.

Involvement may also help students reach their professional goals. Extracurricular activities "might provide evidence for non-cognitive attributes that predict success," writes Dr. Andrew Lee, Chairman of the Department of Ophthalmology at The Methodist Hospital.[35] "Leadership skills demonstrated by being an officer in extracurricular activities or being an Eagle Scout, or a leader or founder of a new organization or club are all looked upon favorably. The second goal is to look for evidence of non-cognitive attributes that might make a superior ophthalmologist (conflict resolution, team work, leadership ability, communication skills, performance under stress, maturity, seriousness of purpose, prior scholarly activity). Finally, programs are looking to graduate (and thus select) residents who will make the program proud."

In fact, extracurricular activities do serve as a significant nonacademic factor in the residency selection process. In a recent NRMP survey of 1,840 program directors representing the nineteen largest medical specialties, 59% of respondents cited volunteer/extracurricular experiences as a factor in selecting applicants to interview.[36]

Evidence suggests that meaningful contributions in extracurricular activities, particularly leadership, may serve as a predictor of residency performance. In one study of emergency medicine residency program directors, having a "distinctive factor" such as being a championship athlete or medical school officer, was one of three factors most predictive of residency performance.[37] In a study to determine predictors of otolaryngology resident success using data available at the time of interview, candidates having an exceptional trait such as leadership experience were found to be rated higher as residents.[38]

Community Service

In researching community service opportunities for medical students, we found ourselves amazed and inspired by the accomplishments of medical schools, medical school organizations, and individual medical students. In Chapter 9, you'll hear about the significant contributions made by students. You'll learn about opportunities for participation in community service, the impact your participation can have on the health of the community, and how your involvement can help you grow personally and professionally.

According to Dr. Aaron McGuffin, Senior Associate Dean for Medical Education at Marshall University School of Medicine, "there has been 2,700 hours of community service donated from the medical school students in the past 12 months. That is a lot of time in addition to doing their medical school work."[39] In 2008, the AAMC found that a significant percentage of medical school applicants had been involved in community service.[40] Sixty-three percent of the applicants reported nonmedical volunteer experience, while medical volunteer experience was reported by 77% of applicants. "They have a real sense of service, commitment, and discovery that I know we all want in a future doctor at our bedside," said Dr. Darrell Kirch, the AAMC President.[41]

While the provision of community service has been a major area of emphasis at U.S. medical schools for years, educators have recently stressed the importance of fostering education in community service among medical students. In 1998, Seifer defined service learning as "a structured learning experience that combines community service with preparation and reflection."[42] The Liaison Committee on Medical Education (LCME), which is responsible for the accreditation of medical schools, recommends that schools should not only provide students with sufficient opportunities "to participate in service-learning activities," but also "encourage and support student participation."[43]

Many schools provide such opportunities for service learning. In 2001, the Morehouse School of Medicine established the Center for Community Health and Service - Learning to engage students and other healthcare professionals in community service and service learning. Partnering with other organizations in the Atlanta area, the center aims to address the health disparities affecting underserved populations. At the University of New Mexico School of Medicine, community service is a key priority.[44] Educators have gone beyond just encouragement by freeing students in the afternoons during the first year for service engagement.

At other schools, student organizations have been able to make significant contributions to their communities. The AAMC's Medicine in the Community Grant Program (formerly known as Caring for Community) offers grant awards to medical students who wish to initiate, develop, and run a community service project.[45] According to the AAMC, "Medicine in the Community will help students to translate great ideas into meaningful service by contributing needed start-up and supplemental funds." Past recipients of the grant include the Medical College of Wisconsin Hmong Health Education Program. HHEP is an effort to improve health education and healthcare services for Wisconsin's Hmong population through educational workshops, outreach programs, support groups, and public service announcements. Another past recipient is the University of New Mexico School of Medicine Community Vision Project. Through the use of mobile eye clinics, basic vision care services are provided to American Indian and Hispanic populations.

For students wishing to make significant contributions to their communities, a number of organizations provide grants and assistance. In this chapter, you'll learn about grants and resources available to students who wish to initiate their own service project, as well as hear about other successful projects. For example, the Medical Student Section of the AMA (AMA-MSS) has created a list and description of projects that AMA-MSS chapters across the country have developed and implemented.[46] Since the 1970s, *Project Bank: The Encyclopedia of Public Health and Community Projects*, a tool offered by the AMA Alliance, has served as a useful compendium of community service projects conducted by state and county Alliances.[47]

Student-run health clinics have been initiated at many medical schools, and such involvement can have a significant impact on the personal and professional growth of medical students. At the University of California Davis, 85% of medical students volunteer in student clinics during their tenure in medical school.[48] "Students are often changed in unexpected, profound, and lasting ways after experiencing firsthand healthcare delivery to the poor, underserved, and marginalized," explains Dr. Ed Farrell, a physician volunteer at the Stout Street Clinic, which is run by students attending the University of Colorado School of Medicine.[49]

Not all schools have initiated such clinics. For motivated students, a number of resources are available for those wishing to establish a student-run health clinic. In an article published in JAMA, Cohen wrote "Eight Steps for Starting a Student-Run Clinic."[50] Another useful resource, "25 Steps to Starting a Student-Run Clinic," is available at the Society of Student-Run Free Clinics website.[51]

Community service provides known benefits to students as well. Research has shown that volunteering increases positive feelings, improves mental health, reduces the risk of depression, and lowers stress levels.[52-54] Participation may also improve communication skills, a vital skill in medicine. Community service is also a significant nonacademic factor in the residency selection process. Once accepted for an interview, the depth and breadth of your involvement in community service may help you stand out in a sea of academically qualified applicants.

Mentoring

The further we've progressed in our own careers, the more it becomes apparent how many individuals have helped us along the way. To achieve professional success in almost any field requires help. This may not be initially obvious to medical students, who are used to studying hard and achieving high grades on their own. Reaching medical school though, definitely required help. Professors who provided help outside of the classroom, researchers who offered the opportunity to participate in their project, advisors who provided letters of recommendation: the list goes on.

Succeeding in medical school, and succeeding in the residency match itself, requires even more assistance. At this next stage of your career, informed guidance and advice becomes even more important. For more competitive specialties or programs, you'll also require additional qualifications, which may mean approaching faculty members for research opportunities, in addition to the critically important letters of recommendation.

The definition of a mentor is one who "takes a special interest in helping another person develop into a successful professional."[55] Information, advice, and guidance from a knowledgeable faculty member is invaluable, and has the potential to impact your career in significant ways.

Sometimes the hardest part of initiating an effective relationship is just knowing how to get started. You'll be approaching respected, accomplished, busy individuals, and it can be difficult to know how to approach faculty members without appearing intrusive or presumptuous. For most students, asking for help from individuals in a position of authority can be intimidating. As a preclinical student, you also may have had limited experience in dealing with faculty on an individual level, and knowing what's acceptable can be hard to determine. Therefore, we provide advice from faculty experienced in this area. Certain approaches would be considered acceptable and non-intrusive by most faculty.

Some medical schools have formal mentoring programs. If such a program doesn't exist at your school, then you'll need confidence and possibly persistence to initiate a relationship. In one study, 28% of students met their mentors during inpatient clerkships, 19% through research activities, and 9% during outpatient clerkships.[56]

Local, regional, and state medical societies may have established mentoring programs. For example, the Santa Clara County Medical Association has a Mentor Program for Stanford medical students.[57] National organizations are committed to mentoring future doctors also. The Society of Academic Emergency Medicine (SAEM) has a medical student virtual advisor program open to students at all institutions.[58] Through this program, students can query experienced individuals about a variety of issues, including the EM residency application process. Dr. Joshua Grossman reminds students that mentors don't have to be in close proximity to you. "Your mentor does not need to be someone involved with your residency program that you see on a daily basis. By sharing your experience with someone removed from the situation you may be able to gain a different and beneficial perspective.[59]

While many of us have worked with assigned advisors during our education, a mentoring relationship is unique, and can be hard to delineate. In Chapter 10, you'll hear from mentors and organizations about the best way to develop such a relationship, and specifics on expectations and etiquette. The Association of Women Surgeons writes "A mentor is a unique individual to you: neither friend, nor colleague, but something of a combination of these and more. Because the relationship differs from those you have with others in your department, you may feel more relaxed and less constrained by professional protocol. This is acceptable to a point, but make certain that you respect the relationship."[60]

What do students talk about with a mentor? Issues may include those related to specialty choice, career satisfaction, wellness, work/life balance, residency selection process, research, interpersonal skills, professionalism, ethics, and courses. Once they have a firm idea of career choice, many students schedule meetings to discuss match strategy, seeking advice on steps they can take at their level to establish their credentials and strengthen their applications.

It can be intimidating and challenging to seek advice from qualified, well-informed faculty members. Is it worth seeking a mentor? While mentors can prove helpful throughout medical school, they can provide invaluable guidance during the process of preparing for the residency match. In researching our companion book, *The Successful Match: 200 Rules to Succeed in the Residency Match*, we asked applicants what they found most difficult about the residency application process. A number of applicants commented on the same issue. "There's so much conflicting information out there. How do you know what to believe? Who should you listen to?" Applicants with mentors have a decided advantage. Students benefit greatly when the wisdom, experience, and perspective of a knowledgeable faculty member are used to help them. Having a mentor to guide you through the complex residency application process is recognized by students as an important factor in boosting the strength of their application.

Well-being

In the past, issues of medical student well-being weren't a priority. Today, though, medical educators recognize that the intense pressures of medical school can have serious consequences for a medical student's physical health and emotional well-being. Research has demonstrated that these aren't just soft issues; they have real ramifications for patient care as well. In a recent study of pediatric residents, 20% of participants met criteria for depression, and these residents made over six times as many medication errors as their non-depressed colleagues.[61]

It's clear that medical school can be intensely stressful. In a survey of medical students, Wolf asked students to rate medical school stressors on a scale of 1 (not stressful) to 7 (extremely stressful).[62] The top four stressors, out of 16 ranked, were examinations, amount of classwork, financial responsibilities, and lack of time for recreation and entertainment. In a survey of medical students at 16 U.S. schools, 60% of first-year students reported either "moderate" or "a lot" of stress in the last two weeks.[63] This stress can lead to physician burnout, a condition which is characterized by emotional depletion from one's work, depersonalization, and the perception that one's work is inconsequential. In a survey of medical students in Minnesota, 45% had burnout.[64]

We chose to emphasize issues of medical student well-being within this chapter for several reasons. One was to highlight the impact of med school stressors on a student's health and well-being. Evidence indicates that this impact can be significant, and it is common for medical students to be affected. Even more importantly, in this chapter you'll learn how to buffer this stress. You'll learn about effective coping strategies identified by researchers. There is significant evidence that sleep, exercise, and the maintenance of strong social connections can provide strong buffers against the stressors of med school. Many students let these activities go first, though, in their efforts to focus on coursework and exams. However, studies indicate that these strategies, and others, should actually be priorities at times of intense stress. In a cross-sectional study of medical students, approximately 77% suffered some degree of anxiety.[65] Anxiety symptoms were considerably less common in students exercising at least 30 minutes three times a week. Another study revealed that "strong social ties was the factor most positively related to better health and life satisfaction" among a group of first-year medical students.[66]

It's important to develop effective coping strategies during the preclinical years, as the clinical care of patients only adds to stress. Dr.

Liselotte Dyrbye, a faculty member at the Mayo Clinic, has performed extensive research in this area. She states that medical students need to have "the skills necessary to assess personal distress, determine its effects on their care of patients, recognize when they need assistance, and develop strategies to promote their own well-being. These skills are essential to maintain perspective, professionalism, and resilience through the course of a career…"[64]

In this chapter, you'll learn more about coping strategies. One effective strategy is problem-focused coping, in which efforts are made to solve or manage the problem causing the distress. Emotion-focused coping is another effective strategy, among many others. As a new med student, it's helpful to learn about how you cope with issues. In 1997, Charles Carver, a professor at the University of Miami, developed the brief COPE questionnaire, which can be used as a tool to help determine the coping strategies that you tend to use.[67] If your total scores are higher in the coping strategy categories of self-distraction, denial, substance abuse, or self-blame, you'll need to learn how to develop and use healthier and more effective coping skills. Dr. Julie Gentile, Director of Medical Student Mental Health Services at the Boonshoft School of Medicine at Wright State University, states that medical school "is a critical period in which to develop and utilize functional and effective coping strategies"[68]

Professionalism

What is professionalism, and why does it matter?

Consider the following observation made by a student:

Two doctors were down the hall from each other, and there were people around. One said to the other, "Did you hear about Mr. X?" And the other doctor said no, and he made a face like a dead face…sticking his tongue out, crossing his eyes, and tilting his head to the side. If anybody had noticed they wouldn't have been too happy with it.[69]

Students must be prepared to deal with issues of professionalism in their peers, in members of the healthcare team, and even in their teachers. Researchers found that exposure to unprofessional behavior began early in the medical education process and increased in each successive year. In Year 1 of medical school, 66% of students had "heard derogatory comments not in patient's presence" and 35% had "observed unethical conduct by residents or attending physicians."[70]

Why else does professionalism matter?

The vast majority of the students we meet have core values and a strong sense of personal integrity. Many therefore assume that issues of professionalism, while they may impact others around them, don't have any relevance to their own behavior. This is due to the common assumption that our core values regarding unethical behavior are stable over time. Studies of medical students contradict this assumption.

In one study, medical students were given a list of 11 unprofessional behaviors, and asked "Is the following behavior unprofessional for a medical student?"[71] Students were surveyed before matriculation and again six months into their first year of medical school. Researchers found that behaviors originally considered unprofessional rapidly became more acceptable. Medical students were also presented with four different scenarios, and asked "Must one do the following to be professional?" For the scenario "Report Cheating to a Professor or Administrator," 69% of students originally answered "yes." Six months into medical school, only 41% answered "yes."

There are therefore two core reasons to focus on this field. If you're a medical student, you are likely to witness lapses in professionalism in patient care, and you need to be prepared to deal with those lapses and protect your patients. You also need to define and protect your own core values and personal integrity.

What is professionalism? The foundation of the medical profession rests upon the trust that patients place in their physicians. Professionalism focuses on this foundation of trust. Although it's been defined in various ways, the core values and elements agreed upon include honesty, integrity, compassion, empathy, ability to communicate effectively with patients, and respect for others. Professionalism is a hot topic in undergraduate medical education. A number of medical education organizations, including the American Board of Internal Medicine, the Association of American Medical Colleges, and the National Board of Medical Examiners, have established professionalism as a required competency across the spectrum of medical education. Medical schools, in turn, have made it a point to educate preclinical students.

Many students, when hearing about a curriculum on professionalism, have similar reactions. "I already hold these values. Why should any of this concern me?" The studies that we describe in this chapter provide a definitive answer to that question. Most students are surprised to learn that the stresses and challenges of medical school can affect attitude, behavior, and conduct. However, this conclusion is clearly supported by a number of studies.

Even though medical students may actually harm patients when they act unethically, such actions persist. In a survey of students at a single medical school, 13 to 24% admitted to cheating during the clinical years of medical school.[72] Examples included "recording tasks not performed" and "lying about having ordered tests." In another study, students were asked whether they had heard of or witnessed unethical behaviors on the part of their student colleagues.[73] In response, 21% had personal knowledge of students "reporting a pelvic examination as 'normal' during rounds when it had been inadvertently omitted from the physical examination."

As students, you are likely to witness lapses in professional behavior, and may witness outright unethical behavior and fraud. These issues affect every level of our profession, and therefore you have to be prepared. You must guard against lapses in your own behavior, and be prepared to deal with lapses in colleagues or supervisors. As physicians, our goal is to treat and protect the patient, and this can be challenging in the real world of clinical medicine.

In a survey, third-year students at the University of Texas Medical Branch at Galveston were asked to evaluate their physicians' professionalism.[74] Although this review of nearly 3,000 evaluation forms revealed significant praise for positive faculty role modeling, negative comments were not infrequent. The majority dealt with "issues of language use, inappropriate use of humor, disrespectful treatment of patients or colleagues, and apparent disinterest in teaching."

Although we think of physicians as highly compassionate and ethical individuals, ethical lapses can extend to the highest levels of our profession. In a stunning case of scientific fraud, Dr. Scott Reuben, a highly regarded anesthesiologist whose research has significantly impacted how physicians treat surgical patients for pain, was found to have fabricated results in over 20 published studies.[75] In some cases, he is alleged to have even invented patients.

Choosing a Specialty

For many students, having just arrived at med school and facing voluminous amounts of material to be learned and retained, the focus will be on just making it through. Why, then, have we devoted a large chapter to the topic of choosing and exploring a specialty?

Those medical students who are able to plan and strategize for the residency match have a decided advantage. For the most competitive specialties, great grades and high USMLE scores are not enough. You'll need great letters of recommendation and support from faculty advocates. You'll also need additional distinctions. Most applicants to the competitive specialties will have performed research, and many will have publications or presentations to their name. Some programs look for additional factors of distinction, such as involvement in extracurricular activities, evidence of leadership, and commitment to service.

We present this information not to scare you, but to prepare you. These are the realities of the residency match today, and students who are prepared for these realities have a definite advantage. Your preparation doesn't need to be an overwhelming experience, either. It can start with the basics, such as exploring different specialties by shadowing faculty or speaking to residents. You may choose to take an aptitude test to help guide you in your exploration of specialties. Many students maximize their free summer after first year by participating in research. Those who are knowledgeable can obtain research grants from organizations to fund their research. This has tangible benefits. It results in research experience, an awarded research grant, and the opportunity to develop a relationship with a research mentor who may be able to support your application down the road.

In this chapter, you'll learn more about how to approach the process of choosing a specialty. You'll learn how to approach your target department, and how to cultivate opportunities. You'll gain from the insider knowledge presented in this section, as the chapter outlines, for each and every specialty, detailed specifics about medical student opportunities. These include mentorship programs, research grants targeted to medical students, and information about national meetings.

Why is it important to at least start thinking about your specialty choice now? While many med students wait until the clinical years to assess fit, this approach can be problematic. At most schools, students are required to rotate through the major or core specialties (internal medicine, general surgery, pediatrics, psychiatry, family medicine, obstetrics & gynecology) before pursuing clerkships in other fields. After completing these core rotations during the third year, students aren't left with much time. Most have two to three months of elective time to explore other specialties before they need to decide, since residency applications are typically submitted in September of the fourth year. For example, in a survey of med schools, it was found that anesthesiology is an elective rotation in 66% of schools.[76] For most students, this means that unless you attend a school with a flexible clerkship curriculum, you won't be able to rotate through the specialty until the beginning of your fourth year.

This can have a decided impact on a student's career. In one study of medical students, 26.2% were unsure of their specialty choice at matriculation.[77] Surprisingly, a similar proportion remained undecided at graduation. According to Gwen Garrison, Director of Student and Applicant Services at the AAMC, 30% of residents "either switch from their intended specialty after a transitional or preliminary year or switch outright during their specialty residency."[78] Dr. George Blackall, Director of Student Development at Penn State University College of Medicine, offers some reasons why residents switch. "Residents primarily switch because they a) realize their initial choice is not as interesting as another specialty, or b) desire a different lifestyle, level of flexibility, or income."[78]

In this chapter, you'll learn how to start the process of exploring a specialty. During the preclinical years, one way to assess fit for specialties is by completing personality-type inventories. The premise of this approach is that people are most satisfied professionally when there is a good match between their specialty choice and their values, skills, and interests. Commonly used assessment methods include the AAMC Careers in Medicine program and the Glaxo Wellcome Pathway Evaluation Program. The AAMC Careers in Medicine (CiM) is a structured program designed to help students gain a better understanding of their personality, values, skills, and interests. The program also allows for exploration of different specialties. The AAMC writes that "as you work through the CiM program, you'll gain the tools to make an informed decision, based on guided self-reflection and the information you'll gather about many career options available to you."[79] Another resource is the Medical Specialty Aptitude Test, an online test developed by the University of Virginia School of Medicine.[80] It is based on content and material from the book, How to Choose a Medical Specialty, by Anita Taylor. The website indicates that "you will be asked to rate your tendencies compared to the tendencies of physicians in each specialty. The higher your score for a given specialty, the more similar you are to the physicians in that specialty."

What is the most important factor in choosing a specialty? In a recent survey of graduating medical students, approximately 97% reported that fit with personality, skills, and interests was moderately or strongly influential in choosing which specialty to pursue as a career.[81] No other factor was given as much importance.

For many students, work/life balance also plays an important role. In the 2010 AAMC Medical School Graduation

Questionnaire, over 11,000 graduating students were asked, "How influential was work/life balance in helping you choose your specialty?"[81] Over 70% of respondents reported work/life balance as being either moderately or strongly influential in their decision-making process. In 1989, Schwartz introduced the term controllable lifestyle to refer to "specialties that offer regular and predictable hours."[82] These specialties are often characterized by fewer hours spent at work and less frequent on-call duties, allowing for greater personal time and flexibility to pursue other activities. Specialties that are generally felt to offer a controllable lifestyle include anesthesiology, dermatology, neurology, ophthalmology, otolaryngology, pathology, psychiatry, and radiology.

Research has shown that efforts to explore specialties during the preclinical years can increase the certainty of specialty choice.[83] In this chapter, you'll learn about multiple avenues to learn more about specialties during the preclinical years. Examples include:

- Identify and work with a mentor
- Volunteer for clinical experiences (e.g., shadowing)
- Perform specialty-specific research
- Meet and speak with as many physicians as you can in your specialties of interest
- Attend local and national specialty organization meetings
- Join specialty interest groups (e.g., Internal Medicine Interest Group, Emergency Medicine Interest Group)

For each of these avenues, we've included specifics on how to proceed. Medical students value mentoring relationships, but identifying and working with a faculty member can be difficult. According to Dr. Gus Garmel, Co-Program Director of the Stanford-Kaiser Emergency Medicine Residency Program, finding a mentor is not easy.[84] "How students find faculty mentors is challenging, because their exposure to a broad selection of emergency medicine faculty may be limited early in their training." We've provided suggestions on how to proceed for each of the specialties. For example, the American College of Physicians (ACP) has created a Mentoring Database. To access the database, which includes program directors, clerkship directors, chairs of medicine, practicing internists, and residents, you must be a member. Mentors are available to answer "specific questions about scheduling your summer preceptorships, getting through the match, and preparing for clerkships and residency interviews..."[85]

We've also included further information about identifying research opportunities. For many of the most competitive specialties, such as dermatology and radiation oncology, your competition will almost all have performed research. Therefore, if you're considering dermatology as a career, you may wish to participate in research between the first and second years of medical school. Research experience has significant educational benefits. Beyond those benefits, research allows a student the chance to develop a relationship with their research supervisor.

In this chapter, you'll gain from the insider knowledge presented for each and every specialty, with detailed, specific information about medical student opportunities.

Chapter excerpted from the book - Success in Medical School: Insider Advice for the Preclinical Years

References

[1]Klatt E, Klatt C. How much is too much reading for medical students? Assigned reading and reading rates at one medical school. *Acad Med* 2011; 86(9): 1079-83.

[2]West C, Sadoski M. Do study strategies predict academic performance in medical school? *Med Educ* 2011; 45(7): 696-703.

[3]Collins G, Cassie J, Daggett C. The role of the attending physician in clinical training. *J Med Educ* 1978; 53: 429-31.

[4]University of Alabama Birmingham School of Medicine. Advice from MS-2 Students. Available at: http://main.uab.edu/uasom/2/show.asp?durki=111766. Accessed October 22, 2011.

[5]Finnerty E, Chauvin S, Bonaminio G, Andrews M, Carroll R, Pangaro L. Flexner revisited: the role and value of the basic sciences in medical education. *Acad Med* 2010; 85 (2): 349-55.

[6]Green M, Jones P, Thomas J. Selection criteria for residency: results of a national program directors survey. *Acad Med* 2009; 84(3): 362-7.

[7]Medscape. The USMLE: Ten Questions. Available at: http://www.medscape.com/viewarticle/403686. Accessed October 19, 2011.

[8]NBME. Available at: http://www.nbme.org. Accessed October 29, 2011.

[9]University of Utah School of Medicine. Preparing for Step 1. Available at: medicine.utah.edu/learningresources/usmle/step1.htm. Accessed October 19, 2011.

[10]University of California San Francisco School of Medicine. Rx for Success on STEP 1 of The Boards. Available at: http://medschool.ucsf.edu/medstudents/documents/step1success.pdf. Accessed October 19, 2011.

[11]NBOME. Available at: http://www.nbome.org. Accessed November 4, 2011.

[12]NRMP. Available at: http://www.nrmp.org. Accessed September 12, 2011.

[13]Cummings M, Sefcik D. The impact of osteopathic physicians' participation in ACGME-accredited postdoctoral programs, 1985-2006. *Acad Med* 2009; 84(6): 733-6.

[14]Moss F, McManus I. The anxieties of new clinical students. *Med Educ* 1992; 26: 17-20.

[15]O'Brien B, Cooke M, Irby D. Perceptions and attributions of third-year student struggles in clerkships: do students and clerkship directors agree? *Acad Med* 2007; 82(10): 970-978.

[16]Windish D, Paulman P, Goroll A, Bass E. Do clerkship directors think medical students are prepared for the clerkship years? *Acad Med* 2004; 79(1): 56-61.

[17]Hauer K, Teherani A, Kerr K, O'Sullivan P, Irby, D. Student performance problems in medical school clinical skills assessments. *Acad Med* 2007; 82(10): S69-S72.

[18]ACP Internist. Good diagnostic skills should begin at the bedside. Available at: http://www.acpinternist.org/archives/2001/02/diagnostics.htm. Accessed February 1, 2012.

[19]Wiener S, Nathanson M. Physical examination: frequently observed errors. *JAMA* 1976; 236(7): 852-5.

[20]Wray N, Friedland J. Detection and correction of house staff error in physical diagnosis. *JAMA* 1983; 249: 1035-7.

[21]Wu E, Fagan M, Reinert S, Diaz J. Self-confidence in and perceived utility of the physical examination: a comparison of medical students, residents, and faculty internists. *J Gen Intern Med* 2007; 22(12): 1725-30.

[22]Conrad P. Learning to doctor: reflections on recent accounts of the medical school years. *Journal of Health and Social Behavior* 1988; 29(4): 323-32.

[23]University of California Davis School of Medicine. Available at: http://mdscholars.ucdavis.edu/Research%20in%20Medical%20School.ppt. Accessed February 9, 2012.

[24]Siemens D, Punnen S, Wong J, Kanji N. A survey on the attitudes towards research in medical school. *BMC Med Educ* 2010; 22: 10: 4.

[25]University of Arizona Medical Student Research Program. Available at: http://www.msrp.medicine.arizona.edu/dist_guidrat.htm. Accessed February 9, 2012.

[26]Dyrbye L, Davidson L, Cook D. Publications and presentations resulting from required research by students at Mayo Medical School, 1976-2003. *Acad Med* 2008; 83(6): 604-10.

[27]Pretorius E. Medical student research: a residency director's perspective. *Acad Radiol* 2002; 9(7): 808-9.

[28]Solomon S, Tom S, Pichert J, Wasserman D, Powers A. Impact of medical student research in the development of physician scientists. *J Investig Med* 2002; 51(3): 149-56.

[29]National Resident Match Program Charting Outcomes in the Match. www.nrmp.org. Accessed August 1, 2010.

[30]Jacobs C, Cross P. The value of medical student research: the experience at Stanford University School of Medicine. *Med Educ* 1995; 29(5): 342-6.

[31]National Student Research Forum. Available at: http://www.utmb.edu/nsrf/. Accessed February 9, 2012.

[32]Zier K, Friedman E, Smith L. Supportive programs increase medical students' research interest and productivity. *J Investig Med* 2006; 54(4): 201-7.

[33]Case Western Reserve University School of Medicine. Available at: http://casemed.case.edu/. Accessed February 12, 2012.

[34]American Medical Association. Available at: http://www.ama-assn.org/ama/pub/about-ama/ama-foundation/our-programs/public-health/excellence-medicine-awards.page. Accessed February 12, 2012.

[35]The Successful Match: Getting into Ophthalmology. Available at: http://studentdoctor.net/2009/08/the-successful-match-interview-with-dr-andrew-lee-ophthalmology/. Accessed February 12, 2012.

[36]NRMP 2010 Program Director Survey. Available at: http://www.nrmp.org/data/index.html. Accessed February 12, 2012.

[37]Hayden S, Hayden M, Garnst A. What characteristics of applicants to emergency medicine residency programs predict future success as an emergency medicine resident. *Acad Emerg Med* 2005; 12(3): 206-10.

[38]Daly K, Levine S, Adams G. Predictors for resident success in otolaryngology. *J Am Coll Surg* 2006; 202 (4): 649-54.

[39]Joan C. Edwards School of Medicine at Marshall University. Available at: http://www.marshallparthenon.com/news/med-students-earning-cash-for-community-service-1.1936252. Accessed September 12, 2011.

[40]Association of American Medical Colleges. Available at: http://www.aamc.org/newsroom/pressrel/2008/enrollmentdata2008.pdf. Accessed July 23, 2011.

[41]American Academy of Family Physicians. Available at: http://www.aafp.org/online/en/home/publications/news/news-now/resident-student-focus/20081119med-school-enroll.html. Accessed February 12, 2012.

[42]Seifer SD. Service-learning: community-campus partnerships for health professions education. *Acad Med* 1998; 73(3): 273-7.

[43]Liaison Committee on Medical Education (LCME) Available at: http://www.lcme.org/standard.htm#servicelearning. Accessed February 12, 2012.

[44]University of New Mexico School of Medicine. Available at: http://hsc.unm.edu/som/. Accessed February 22, 2012.

[45]AAMC Medicine in the Community Grant Program. Available at: http://www.aamc.org/about/awards/cfc/start.htm. Accessed February 12, 2012.

[46]American Medical Association Medical Student Section. Available at: http://www.ama-assn.org. Accessed February 12, 2012.

[47]AMA Alliance Project Bank. Available at: http://www.amaalliance.org/site/epage/40331_625.htm. Accessed February 12, 2012.

[48]University of California Davis School of Medicine. Available at: http://www-med.ucdavis.edu/. Accessed September 12, 2011.

[49]American Medical Association Virtual Mentor. Available at: http://virtualmentor.ama-assn.org/2005/07/medu1-0507.html. Accessed February 12, 2012.

[50]Cohen J. Eight Steps for starting a student-run clinic. *JAMA* 1995; 273: 434–5.

[51]Society of Student-Run Free Clinics. Available at: http://www.studentrunfreeclinics.org/index.php?option=com_content&view=article&id=65&Itemid=144. Accessed February 12, 2012.

[52]Thoits P, Hewitt L. Volunteer work and well-being. *Journal of Health and Social Behavior* 2001; 42(2): 115-31.

[53]Van Willigen M. Differential benefits of volunteering across the life course. *The Journals of Gerontology Series B: Psychological Sciences and Social Sciences* 2000; 55B(5): S308-S318.

[54]Rietschlin J. Voluntary association membership and psychological distress. *J Health Soc Behav* 1998; 39; 348-55.

[55]Adviser, teacher, role model, friend. Available at: http://stills.nap.edu/readingroom/books/mentor. Accessed March 13, 2008. Washington, DC: National Academy Press; 1997.

[56]Aagaard E, Hauer K. A cross-sectional descriptive study of mentoring relationships formed by medical students. *J Gen Intern Med* 2003; 18: 298-302.

[57]Santa Clara County Medical Association Mentor Program for Stanford medical students. Available at: http://med.stanford.edu/mentors/. Accessed February 9, 2012.

[58]Society of Academic Emergency Medicine (SAEM). Available at: http://www.saem.org/e-advising-faqs-students. Accessed February 9, 2012.

[59]American College of Physicians. Finding the right mentor for you. Available at: http://www.acponline.org/medical_students/impact/archives/2010/11/feature/. Accessed February 9, 2012.

[60]Association of Women Surgeons. Available at: https://www.womensurgeons.org/CDR/Mentorship.asp. Accessed February 9, 2012.

[61]Fahrenkopf A, Sectish T, Barger L, Sharek P, Lewin D, Chiang V, Edwards S, Wiedermann B, Landrigan C. Rates of medication errors among depressed and burnt out residents: prospective cohort study. *BMJ* 2008; 336(7642): 488-91.

[62]Wolf T, Faucett J, Randall H, Balson P. Graduating medical students' ratings of stresses, pleasures, and coping strategies. *J Med Educ* 1988; 63(8): 636-42.

[63]Compton M, Carrera J, Frank E. Stress and depressive symptoms/dysphoria among US medical students: results from a large, nationally representative survey. *J Nerv Ment Dis* 2008; 196(12): 891-7.

[64]Dyrbye L, Thomas M, Huntington J, Lawson K, Novotny P, Sloan J, Shanafelt T. Personal life events and medical student burnout: a multicenter study. *Acad Med* 2006; 81 (4): 374-84.

[65]Hussein E, Gabr A, Mohamed A, Hameed A. Physical exercise and anxiety among medical students at Ain Shams University. Presented at the 13th Annual International Ain Shams Medical Students' Congress, Feb 14-16, 2005.

[66]Parkerson G, Broadhead W, Tse C. The health status and life satisfaction of first-year medical students. *Acad Med* 1990; 65(9): 586-8.

[67]Carver C. You want to measure coping but your protocol's too long: consider the brief COPE. *International Journal of Behavioral Medicine* 1997; 4: 92-100.

[68]Gentile J, Roman B. Medical student mental health services; psychiatrists treating medical students. *Psychiatry* 2009; 6(5): 38-45.

[69]Baernstein A, Oelschlager A, Chang T, Wenrich M. Learning professionalism: perspectives of preclinical medical students. *Acad Med* 2009; 84(5): 574-81.

[70]Satterwhite W, Satterwhite R, Enarson C. Medical students' perceptions of unethical conduct at one medical school. *Acad Med* 1998; 73(5): 529-531.

[71]Humphrey H, Smith K, Reddy S, Scott D, Madara J, Arora V. Promoting an environment of professionalism: The University of Chicago "Roadmap." *Acad Med* 2007; 82(11): 1098-1107.

[72]Dans P. Self-reported cheating by students at one medical school. *Acad Med* 1996; 71 (1, suppl): S70-72.

[73]Anderson R, Obenshain S. Cheating by students: findings, reflections, and remedies. *Acad Med* 1994; 69(5): 323-332.

[74]Szauter K, Turner H. Using students' perceptions of internal medicine teachers' professionalism. *Acad Med* 2001; 76(5): 575-6.

[75]Kowalczyk L. Doctor accused of faking studies. *The Boston Globe*; March 11, 2009.

[76]Lin S, Strom S, Canales C, Rodriguez A, Kain Z. The impact of the anesthesiology clerkship structure on medical students matched to anesthesiology. Abstract presented at the 2010 Annual Meeting of the American Society Anesthesiologists. A1106.

[77]Kassebaum D, Szenas P. Medical students' career indecision and specialty rejection: roads not taken. *Acad Med* 1995; 70(10): 937-43.

[78]Association of American Medical Colleges. Available at: http://www.aamc.org/students/cim/august10choices.pdf. Accessed November 21, 2011.

[79]Association of American Medical Colleges (AAMC). Available at: http://www.aamc.org/students/cim/about.htm. Accessed September 23, 2011.

[80]University of Virginia School of Medicine Medical Specialty Aptitude Test. Available at: http://www.med-ed.virginia.edu/specialties. Accessed January 24, 2012.

[81]2010 AAMC Medical School Graduation Questionnaire. Available at: http://www.aamc.org. Accessed August 13, 2011.

[82]Dorsay E, Jarjoura D, Rutecki G. Influence of controllable lifestyle on recent trends in specialty choice by US medical students. *JAMA* 2003; 290(9): 1173-8.

[83]Weinstein P, Gipple C. Some determinants of career choice in the second year of medical school. *J Med Educ* 1975; 50(2): 194-8.

[84]Garmel G. Mentoring medical students in academic emergency medicine. *Acad Emerg Med* 2004; 11(12): 1351-7.

[85]ACP Mentoring Database. Available at: http://www.acponline.org/residents+fellows/mentors/. Accessed January 25, 2012.

An excerpt from the best-selling book:
Success on the Wards:
250 Rules for Clerkship Success

By Dr. Samir P. Desai
and Dr. Rajani Katta

Chapter 1

Third Year of Medical School

Rule # 1   **You came to medical school to be a great doctor. That process begins now.**

Why did you become a doctor? There may be a number of reasons, but the most important one is the same across the board: to take care of patients. You will read startling amounts of information during medical school, and your training will include many procedures and new techniques, but all of it is in the service of patient care. You are here to make each and every individual patient better.

That process starts now.

It is an amazing privilege to take care of patients. You can read about a disease all that you want, but to be able to speak to and examine a patient with that disease is an unsurpassed learning experience. It is an incredible responsibility as well. You will be asking patients the most intimate and intrusive types of questions. You will be asking patients to offer their arm for a needle, to disrobe for an exam, to let you literally poke and prod at their body. In return, you are responsible for protecting them from harm, and for healing them.

Starting as a medical student, and progressing to a respected physician, is a long, difficult, and intense process. It takes years of education, and years of training. The privileges granted to physicians are remarkable. In return, you have a great responsibility. Your education is in the service of patient care. You have a responsibility to make the most of that education.

What does it take to be a great doctor? There is an impressive body of research devoted to medical student education, and to the factors and interventions that ensure good doctors. Medical educators work hard to ensure that students master these different facets of the practice of medicine.

Why are clerkships so important to the process of producing great doctors?

The areas emphasized in clerkships are those that are integral to becoming a great physician.

Patient care requires the daily use of many skills. On a daily basis, a physician may need to:

- Obtain an accurate medication history.
- Detect a heart murmur.
- Create a differential diagnosis for the patient with abdominal pain.
- Interpret an elevated alkaline phosphatase.
- Formulate a management plan for the patient with a myocardial infarction.
- Communicate that plan through oral discussions and written documentation.
- Utilize the talents of an entire health care team to maximize patient care.
- Manifest their concern for the patient in every interaction.

Clerkships teach students how to accomplish these difficult, vital skills.

If you don't learn certain skills in medical school, you may never learn them.

Clinical clerkships provide the foundation of successful patient care. They represent a critical time in your education. If you want to become proficient in exam skills, you have to learn now. These aren't skills you can learn from reading a textbook. You need to evaluate patients with these findings, and you need to have a teacher that can demonstrate these findings. You need to be able to ask questions freely in order to learn all the finer points of physical exam skills. This isn't something you can easily do as a resident, and certainly not as a board-certified physician. If you don't know how to assess jugular venous distention by the end of medical school, you may never learn.

While you would assume that medical school teaches you everything you need to know to function well as a resident, that isn't true for all students, particularly those who take a passive approach to learning or those who focus their education on textbook learning. You need to maximize your learning experiences and teaching opportunities on the wards. Passive learning has real consequences.

In one eye-opening study, internal medicine residents were tested on cardiac auscultatory skills. They listened to 12 prerecorded cardiac events. American residents demonstrated poor proficiency, with mean identification rates of only 22%.[1] In another study of resident skills, ECG proficiency was measured. Surprisingly, 58% of residents wrongly diagnosed complete heart block, and only 22% were certain of their diagnosis of ventricular tachycardia.[2] In a study of radiologic proficiency, participants included mainly residents, with some students. In x-rays representing emergency situations, pneumothorax was misdiagnosed by 91% of participants overall, while a misplaced central venous catheter was missed by 74%.[3]

Skills in patient examination, interpretation of tests, synthesis of information, and medical decision-making are honed through years of practice. Clerkships are only the first step, but provide an invaluable education, with supervisors there to demonstrate, to model, and to teach skills. The best medical students regard clerkships as a unique and invaluable learning experience, difficult to replicate in residency or later through seminars and conferences.

If you don't learn it now, you may have problems as a resident.

Medical school is the time to learn and develop your clinical skills. It's also the time to develop and hone the learned attributes and attitudes that predict success as a physician. In a study of residents with problematic behavior, investigators sought to determine if there were prognostic indicators in their medical school evaluations.[4] The short answer is yes.

Students whose evaluations indicated that they were timid, had problems in organization, displayed little curiosity, and had difficulty applying knowledge clinically, among other types, were more likely to become problem residents. The authors "found a rather robust multilevel correlation between residents who have problems, major or minor, during or after residency, and negative statements, even subtle ones, in the dean's letter." The predictive statements noted in the dean's letter included:

Very nervous, timid initially/ Displayed little curiosity/ Had difficulty applying knowledge clinically/ He came across as confrontational/ Maybe somewhat overconfident for his level of training/ Lack of enthusiasm and problems in organization/
Needs to read more on her own/ Lots of effort, uneven outcome

Difficulties during clerkships may predict difficulties as a physician, including disciplinary actions by the State Medical Board.

Clerkships are the foundation of successful patient care. During clerkships, medical students also develop and hone the attributes and attitudes that are required of successful physicians. These are referred to collectively as medical professionalism. "The specific attributes that have long been understood to animate professionalism include altruism, respect, honesty, integrity, dutifulness, honour, excellence and accountability."[5] –Dr. Jordan Cohen, President Emeritus, Association of American Medical Colleges

If you don't hone these traits during medical school, you may have problems as a physician. Unprofessional behavior in medical school is a possible predictor of future disciplinary action. A particularly notable study was performed by Dr. Maxine Papadakis, associate dean for student affairs at the UCSF School of Medicine. She and her team examined the medical school records of 235 graduates of three medical schools. Each of these physicians had been disciplined by one of 40 state medical boards over a 13-year period. The disciplined physicians were three times more likely than a control group to have negative comments about their professionalism documented in their medical school record.[6]

Another study sought to identify the domains of unprofessional behavior in medical school that were associated with disciplinary action by a state medical board.[7] Three domains of unprofessional behavior were significantly associated with future disciplinary action: poor reliability and responsibility, poor initiative and motivation, and lack of self-improvement and adaptability.

Your core clerkship grades may either limit or expand your future career options.

The skills and traits reflected in core clerkship grades are considered so important to future success as a resident that residency programs use these grades as a major criteria in the selection process. Program directors are decision-makers in the residency selection process. In a survey of over 1,200 residency program directors across 21 medical specialties, grades in required clerkships were ranked as the # 1 factor used in the selection process.[8]

Studies across multiple specialties have supported the predictive nature of clerkship grades. In one study, researchers sought to determine which residency selection criteria had the strongest correlation with performance as an orthopedic surgery resident. The authors concluded that the "number of honors grades on clinical rotations was the strongest predictor of performance."[9] In a study of physical medicine and rehabilitation residents, "clinical residency performance was predicted by clerkship grade honors."[10] In one study of internal medicine residents, performance as a resident was significantly associated with the internal medicine clerkship grade.[11]

In the next 400 plus pages, we review each of the areas that students need to master in clerkships. The book contains a great deal of in-depth content across a range of areas vital to medical student success. It's also arranged to ensure ease of use. The first sections serve as straightforward how-to guides for each of the core clerkships. If you're starting your Pediatrics clerkship, and aren't sure how to write the daily patient progress note, Chapter 4 walks you through that process. If you're starting the Ob/Gyn clerkship, and don't know how to write a delivery note, Chapter 6 provides a template and sample note that details exactly what you'll need to include. The latter chapters provide more wide-ranging content. If you'll be presenting in rounds for the first time, you can turn to the chapter on oral case presentations and review the features you'll need to include. If you are committed to fully protecting your patients from the hazards of hospitalization, Chapter 8 Patients includes several tables that outline the steps that medical students can take, even at their level, to protect their patients. Chapter 22 reviews the impact of collaborative care on patient outcomes, and provides recommendations that students can implement.

The recommendations presented here are based on discussions with numerous faculty members, residents, and students, as well as our own experiences. We've also focused our efforts on evidence-based advice. This evidence-based advice is based on our review of the substantial medical literature in the area of medical student education. The book includes over 400 references from the relevant literature.

Over the next 400 plus pages, you'll learn how to maximize your education during core clerkships, as well as your performance. Your success on the wards will become the foundation of outstanding patient care.

Patients

We begin this chapter with one of the most famous quotes in the history of medicine. "First, do no harm." From ancient times onwards, medical practice has posed dangers to patients. In modern times, those dangers are shockingly common. Medical error is thought to be the <u>third</u>

leading case of death in the US.[12] Those errors include the unbelievable: one report described an average of 27 cases in one year, per New York hospital, of invasive procedures performed on the wrong patient.[13] Some of those dangers have become so commonplace that we consider them routine. When a patient develops a hospital-related infection, we document it as a nosocomial infection and treat the infection without questioning why it occurred. However, many of those infections are preventable, and should never have occurred at all. In this chapter, we document a number of specific measures that medical students can implement to protect their patients, from the use of standardized abbreviations to ensuring that patients receive venous thromboembolism prophylaxis when indicated. We outline how medical students can identify the hazards of hospitalization, thus ensuring that you can act to mitigate those hazards. We review nosocomial infections, and how you may be a culprit through your hands, your clothing, and even your stethoscope.

We also review the type of skills that ensure that patients feel comfortable with your care. The best medical care necessitates that patients trust their physicians and have confidence in both their abilities and the fact that the physician cares about the patient, not just the illness. In this chapter, our focus is on the patient, and how medical students can improve the care provided to patients. We outline steps that students can take, even at their level, to protect their patients from physical harm. We emphasize the different ways in which medical students can enhance patient care, patient education, and patient counseling. On a daily basis, you have the opportunity and the power to enhance the care provided to your patients.

Internal Medicine Clerkship

The field of internal medicine (IM) has a broad impact on all fields of medicine. "Learning about internal medicine – the specialty providing comprehensive care to adults – in the third year of medical school is an important experience, regardless of what specialty the medical student ultimately pursues," says Dr. Patrick Alguire, the Director of Education and Career Development at the American College of Physicians.[14] Through this clerkship, you will hone your skills in history and physical examination, diagnostic test interpretation, medical decision-making, and management of core medical conditions. These skills are important ones for all physicians, even if you ultimately decide to enter radiology, pathology, emergency medicine, or another field. Overall, internal medicine does stand as the most frequently chosen specialty in the residency match. In 2010, over 3,000 allopathic and osteopathic medical students matched into an internal medicine residency program.

Your IM clerkship grade can impact your career. It's a factor in the residency selection process for all specialties, not just internal medicine. In a survey of over 1,200 residency program directors across 21 medical specialties, grades in required clerkships were ranked as the # 1 factor used in the selection process.[8] "Do well in your clerkship," writes the Department of Medicine at the University of Washington. "Yes, this is obvious – and easier said than done – but it's also important. Most residency programs look closely at the third-year clerkship grade when selecting applicants."[15]

Many medical students find this clerkship formidable. A lack of knowledge isn't the main factor. The main factor is a lack of preparation for your many responsibilities. How do I evaluate a newly admitted patient? What do I need to include in a daily progress note? What information do I need to include in a comprehensive write-up? How do I present newly admitted patients to the attending physician?

In this chapter, templates and outlines are included for each of these important responsibilities. You'll also find a number of tips and suggestions on how to maximize your learning and performance during this rotation. You'll find detailed information that will help you effectively pre-round, succeed during work rounds, deliver polished oral case presentations, create well-written daily progress notes, and generate comprehensive write-ups.

For students interested in a career in internal medicine, this chapter also details how to strengthen your application. You'll learn how to identify potential mentors and obtain strong letters of recommendation. You'll learn about recommended electives and sub-internships, as well as specifics that detail how to maximize the impact of your application.

Surgery Clerkship

The surgery clerkship provides significant exposure to common surgical problems, and allows you to evaluate the specialty as a potential career choice. Although the bulk of your education will take place on the general surgery service, most rotations provide the opportunity to explore several surgical subspecialties. A surgical clerkship education is very valuable, whether or not you choose to practice in a surgical field. Primary care physicians must be familiar with the evaluation and management of patients in the pre-operative and post-operative settings. An understanding of core surgical principles is important across many fields, including ones such as anesthesiology, dermatology, and emergency medicine. From a personal standpoint, you or a family member is likely to undergo surgery in your lifetime, and you'll find that an understanding of the pre-operative, operative, and post-operative stages will be valuable.

Regardless of your chosen career, your surgery clerkship grade will be a factor used in the residency selection process, due to an emphasis on core clerkship grades in the residency selection process. In a survey of over 1,200 residency program directors across 21 medical specialties, grades in required clerkships were ranked as the # 1 factor used in the selection process.[8] The University of Colorado Department of Surgery writes that "most surgery programs look very favorably on an 'Honors' grade in your MS3 surgery clerkship rotation and may factor in the grades you received in your Medicine and Ob/Gyn rotations."[16] It's not easy to honor the clerkship. In a survey of medical schools across the country, Takayama found that only 27% of students achieve the highest grade in the surgery clerkship.[17]

Many students approach the surgery clerkship with considerable anxiety. In one study, students were most concerned about fatigue, long hours, workload, insufficient sleep, lack of time to study, mental abuse (getting yelled at or relentless pimping), and poor performance.[18] Unfamiliarity with the operating room environment was also concerning.

In the Surgery Clerkship chapter, we provide tips for operating room success, a checklist for thorough pre-rounding, a step-by-step guide to presenting patients, and time-saving templates for the pre-op, post-op, and op notes. This information will maximize your education as well as your performance.

In 2010, approximately 2,500 allopathic and osteopathic medical students matched into general surgery or related surgical specialty, such as ophthalmology, orthopedic surgery, otolaryngology, plastic surgery, or urology. This chapter includes recommendations for those students interested in pursuing general surgery as a career. When should you do a sub-internship? Should you do an away elective? What are considered negatives in a residency application? These questions, and others, are answered.

Excerpted from the book – Success on the Wards: 250 Rules for Clerkship Success.

Read more of the first chapter at www.TheSuccessfulMatch.com

THE MEDICAL SCHOOL INTERVIEW

An excerpt from the best-selling book:
The Successful Match:
200 Rules to Succeed in the Residency Match

By Dr. Rajani Katta
and Dr. Samir P. Desai

Chapter 1

The Application

What does it take to match successfully? What does it take to match into the specialty and program of your choice?

In the 2011 Match, over 40% of all U.S. senior applicants failed to match at the program of their choice. In competitive fields such as urology, orthopedic surgery, and plastic surgery, over 23% of U.S. senior applicants failed to match at all.

Percentage of U.S. senior applicants who failed to match in 2011	
Specialty	**% of U.S. seniors failing to match**
Plastic surgery	56%
Orthopedic surgery	23%
Urology	23%
Dermatology	21%
General surgery	20%
Radiation oncology	15%
Otolaryngology	14%
Neurological surgery	14%
Ophthalmology	10%
From www.nrmp.org, www.sfmatch.org, www.auanet.org.	

The numbers are significantly worse for osteopathic and international medical graduates:

- 28% of the 2,200 osteopathic students and graduates who participated in the 2011 Match failed to match at all.
- 57% of the 10,400 international medical graduates who participated in the 2011 Match failed to match at all.

Did you know…

Applicants who fail to match may participate in the Match Week Supplemental Offer and Acceptance Program (SOAP), which was launched in 2012 to replace the Scramble. Using SOAP, applicants can try to match at a program that didn't fill. In 2012, over 12,000 applicants were eligible for only 1,100 positions.

What does it actually take to match successfully? The issue is a hotly debated one, and surveys of students, reviews of student discussion forums, and discussions with academic faculty all find sharp divisions on the topic. In the following 400 plus pages, we answer the question of what it takes to match successfully. We also provide specific evidence-based advice to maximize your chances of a successful match.

Our recommendations are based on data from the full spectrum of sources. We present evidence obtained from scientific study and published in the academic medical literature. The results of these studies can provide a powerful impetus for specific actions. We present anecdotal data and advice that has been published in the literature and obtained from online sources. We also provide an insider's look at the entire process of residency selection based on our experiences, the experiences of our colleagues in the world of academic medicine, and the experiences of students and residents with whom we have worked.

Who actually chooses the residents? We review the data on the decision-makers. What do these decision-makers care about? We review the data on the criteria that matter to them. How can you convince them that you would be the right resident for their program? We provide concrete, practical recommendations based on this data. At every step of the process, our recommendations are meant to maximize the impact of your application.

In Chapter 2, starting on page 21, we present specialty-specific data. Given the high failure to match rates for certain specialties, is there any literature available to applicants to guide them through the residency application process? For each specialty, we present the results of those studies. For example, in radiology, a 2006 survey of residency program directors obtained data from 77 directors on the criteria that programs use to select their residents (Otero). Which criteria did these directors rank as most important in deciding whom to interview? Which selection factors were most important in determining an applicant's place on the program's rank order list? What were the mean USMLE step 1 scores among matched and unmatched U.S. seniors? What percentage of U.S. seniors who matched were members of the Alpha Omega Alpha Honor Medical Society (AOA)? This powerful evidence-based information is data that you must have to develop an application strategy that maximizes your chances of a successful match.

We review each component of the application in comprehensive detail in the following chapters. Each single component of your application can be created, modified, or influenced in order to significantly strengthen your overall candidacy. We devote the next 400 plus pages to showing you, in detail, exactly how to do so.

LETTERS OF RECOMMENDATION

Letters of recommendation are a critical component of the residency application. Since you won't be directly writing these letters, it may seem as if you have no control over their content. In reality, you wield more influence than you realize. In our chapter on letters of recommendation, we detail the steps that you can take in order to have the best possible letters written on your behalf. These steps include choosing the correct letter writers and asking in the correct manner. We also discuss the type of information to provide, and the manner in which to provide it, in order to highlight those qualities that you hope your letter writer will emphasize.

The purpose of these letters is to emphasize that you have the professional qualifications needed to excel. The letters should also demonstrate that you have the personal qualities to succeed as a resident and, later, as a practicing physician. Since these letters are written by those who know you and the quality of your work, they offer programs a personalized view. In contrast to your transcript and USMLE scores, they supply programs with qualitative, rather than quantitative, information about your cognitive and non-cognitive characteristics.

What do the faculty members reviewing applications look for in a letter of recommendation? The first item noted is the writer of the letter. In a survey of program directors in four specialties (internal medicine, pediatrics, family medicine, and surgery), it was learned that a candidate's likelihood of being considered was enhanced if there was a connection or relationship between the writer and residency program director (Villanueva). "In cases where there was both a connection between the faculty members and in-depth knowledge of the student (i.e., personal knowledge), the likelihood was that the student's application would be noted." In a survey of 109 program directors of orthopedic surgery residency programs, 54% of directors agreed that the most important aspect of a letter was that it was written by someone that they knew (Bernstein).

In another study, the academic rank of the writer was found to be an important factor influencing the reviewer's ranking of the letter (Greenburg). 48% of the reviewers rated it as important. A survey of physical medicine and rehabilitation (PM&R) program directors asked respondents to rate the importance of letters of recommendation in selecting residents (DeLisa). The study showed that the "most important letters of recommendation were from a PM&R faculty member in the respondent's department, followed by the dean's letter, and the PM&R chairman's letter." Next in importance were letters from a PM&R faculty member in a department other than the respondents', followed by a clinical faculty member in another specialty. The University of Texas-Houston Medical School Career Counseling Catalog gives this advice: "letters of recommendation from private physicians or part-time faculty, and letters from residents are generally discounted."

For internal medical graduates (IMGs), this issue becomes even more important. A survey of 102 directors of internal medicine residency programs sought to determine the most important predictors of performance for IMGs (Gayed). When rating the importance of 22 selection criteria, the lowest rated criterion was letters of recommendation from a foreign country, with 93% of program directors feeling that such letters were useless.

What else do the faculty members reviewing applications look for in a letter of recommendation? They seek evidence of an applicant's strengths and skills. Most applicants assume that their letter writers know what to say and what information to provide in a letter to substantiate their recommendation. However, that's a dangerous assumption. In an analysis of 116 recommendation letters received by the radiology residency program at the University of Iowa Hospitals & Clinics (O'Halloran), reviewers noted that:

- 10% of letters were missing information about an applicant's cognitive knowledge
- 35% of letters had no information about an applicant's clinical judgment
- 3% of letters did not discuss an applicant's work habits
- 17% of letters did not comment on the applicant's motivation
- 32% of letters were lacking information about interpersonal communication skills

In another review of recommendation letters sent during the 1999 application season to the Department of Surgery at Southern Illinois University, writers infrequently commented on psychomotor skills such as "easily performed minor procedures at the bedside," "good eye-hand coordination in the OR," "could suture well," and so on (Fortune).

Our chapter on letters of recommendation, starting on page 159, reviews strategies to locate those letter writers who will be most helpful to your candidacy. We review how to identify these writers and how to approach them. Most importantly, we discuss the type of evidence you can provide to the writer and the professional manner in which to provide it. Your letter writers want to write the best letter possible, and you can do much more than you realize to make this a reality.

Excerpted from the book - The Successful Match: 200 Rules to Succeed in the Residency Match.

Read more of the first chapter at www.TheSuccessfulMatch.com.

THE MEDICAL SCHOOL INTERVIEW

Success in Medical School: Insider Advice for the Preclinical Years

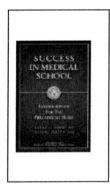

By Samir P. Desai, MD and Rajani Katta, MD

ISBN # 9781937978006

According to the AAMC, the United States will have a shortage of 90,000 physicians by 2020. In the mid-1990s, the AAMC urged medical schools to expand enrollment. Class sizes have increased, and new schools have opened their doors. Unfortunately, rising enrollment in medical schools has not led to a corresponding increase in the number of residency positions.

As a result, medical students are finding it increasingly difficult to match with the specialty and program of their choice. "Competition is tightening," said Mona Signer, Executive Director of the National Resident Matching Program. "The growth in applicants is more than the increase in positions."

Now more than ever, preclinical students need to be well informed so that they can maximize their chances of success. The decisions you make early in medical school can have a significant impact on your future specialty options.

To build a strong foundation for your future physician career, and to match into your chosen field, you must maximize your preclinical education. In *Success in Medical School*, you'll learn specific strategies for success during these important years of medical school.

"Overall, I recommend this book...The book has so much information about everything that there has to be a part of the book that will satisfy your interests."

-    Medical School Success website

Clinician's Guide to Laboratory Medicine: Pocket

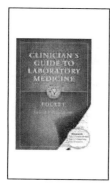

By Samir P. Desai, MD

ISBN # 9780972556187

In this book, you will find practical approaches to lab test interpretation. It includes differential diagnoses, step-by-step approaches, and algorithms, all designed to answer your lab test questions in a flash. See why so many consider it a "must-have" book.

"In our Medicine Clerkship, the Clinician's Guide to Laboratory Medicine has quickly become one of the two most popular paperback books. Our students have praised the algorithms, tables, and ease of pursuit of clinical problems through better understanding of the utilization of tests appropriate to the problem at hand."

- Greg Magarian, MD, Director, 3rd Year Internal Medicine Clerkship, Oregon Health & Science University

"It provides an excellent practical approach to abnormal labs."

- Northwestern University Feinberg School of Medicine Internal Medicine Clerkship website.

THE MEDICAL SCHOOL INTERVIEW

Success on the Wards: 250 Rules for Clerkship Success

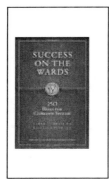

By Samir P. Desai, MD and Rajani Katta, MD

ISBN # 9780972556194

This is an absolute must-read for students entering clinical rotations.

The authors of *The Successful Match: 200 Rules to Succeed in the Residency Match* bring their same combination of practical recommendations and evidence-based advice to clerkships.

The book begins as a how-to guide with clerkship-specific templates, along with sample notes and guides, for every aspect of clerkships. The book reviews proven strategies for success in patient care, write-ups, rounds, and other vital areas.

Grades in required rotations are the most important academic criteria used to select residents, and this critical year can determine career choices. This book shows students what they can do now to position themselves for match success. An invaluable resource for medical students - no student should be without it.

"*Success on the Wards* is an essential tool for the rising medical student...This book offers insider information on how a medical student can excel on the wards…I strongly recommend this book. It should be a must-read for any motivated student doctor."

-    AMSA *The New Physician* (Review from September 2012)

"*Success on the Wards* is easily the best book I have read on how to succeed in clerkship. It is comprehensive, thorough and jam-packed with valuable information. Dr. Desai and Dr. Katta provide an all encompassing look into what clerkship is really like."

-    Review by Medaholic.com

The Successful Match: 200 Rules to Succeed in the Residency Match

By Rajani Katta, MD and Samir P. Desai, MD

ISBN # 9780972556170

What does it take to match into the specialty and program of your choice?

The key to a successful match hinges on the development of the right strategy. This book will show you how to develop the optimal strategy for success.

Who actually chooses the residents? We review the data on the decision-makers. What do these decision-makers care about? We review the data on the criteria that matter most to them. How can you convince them that you would be the right resident for their program? We provide concrete, practical recommendations based on their criteria.

At every step of the process, our recommendations are meant to maximize the impact of your application. This book is an invaluable resource to help you gain that extra edge.

"Drs. Rajani Katta and Samir P. Desai provide the medical student reader with detailed preparation for the matching process. The rules and accompanying tips make the book user-friendly. The format is especially appealing to those pressed for time or looking for a single key element for a particular process."

- Review in the American Medical Student Association journal, *The New Physician*

The Successful Match website

Our website, TheSuccessfulMatch.com, provides medical school applicants with a better understanding of the admissions process. You'll find:

- Inside look at the medical school admissions process
- Profiles of medical schools
- Advice from the decision-makers
- Tips to help you tailor your interview answers from school to school
- Resources to help you succeed in the preclinical years and clerkships
- Information to position yourself for residency match success

Consulting services

We also offer expert one-on-one consulting services to premedical and medical students. For premedical students, mock interview services are available with Dr. Samir Desai. Dr. Desai has years of experience interviewing applicants, and will offer you a detailed strategy for success tailored to your medical school of interest. We have the knowledge, expertise, and insight to help you achieve your goals. If you are interested in our consultation services, please visit us at www.TheSuccessfulMatch.com. The website provides further details, including pricing and specific services.

MD2B Titles

The Medical School Interview: Winning Strategies from Admissions Faculty

Success in Medical School: Insider Advice for the Preclinical Years

Success on the Wards: 250 Rules for Clerkship Success

The Successful Match: 200 Rules to Succeed in the Residency Match

Clinician's Guide to Laboratory Medicine: Pocket

Available at www.MD2B.net

Bulk Sales

MD2B is able to provide discounts on any of our titles when purchased in bulk. The discount rate depends on the quantity ordered. For more information, please contact us at info@md2b.net or (713) 927-6830.